Born in Chechnya

Olga McPhail

Mira Publishing House CIC.
PO BOX 312
Leeds LS16 0FN
West Yorkshire
England
www.MiraPublishing.com

Born In Chechnya
By Olga McPhail
ISBN: 978-1-908509-07-9
First published in Great Britain 2013 by Mira Publishing House CIC.

Printed and bound by www.beamreachuk.co.uk

A full CIP record for this book is available from the British Library.
A full CIP record for this book is available from the Library of Congress.

Mira Intelligent Read

Chechnya. My love-hate relationship. My birthplace. Forever imprinted in my passport, my memory, my fate. I started this book in May 1991. I could not sleep that night. I did not dare to lie down and close my eyes, needed to be on guard. The lines coming out of my ancient typewriter somehow helped me to keep an illusion of staying in control. Otherwise an overwhelming fear would come out of the corners of my conscious, creeping into my limbs, my stomach, my heart, sending cold sweat out of every pore of my body. 'No, no! Stop it!' I said to myself. The front door was locked. The heavy metal bar was put across it. 'They are safe, my girls,' I kept repeating, making my inner voice sound as convincing as possible. My grandmother had joined my two daughters under the general title of "the girls" long ago, when she moved in with us after grandfather's death. I hoped the clicking sound of typing coming from my room would give them the illusion of normality. I put my name on the front page: Sofia Zelinskaya. It is my maiden name. I kept it after I married in memory of my father who did not live long enough to have a son.

The First Chapter of Sofia's Book,

written during the Night of the Jail Riot

I like my new apartment. You could not tell that it is less than a year since we moved in, we have put so much effort into making it a home. The best thing is its location. It is only a fifteen minute walk from the centre, away from the main road, but not far from it. And the school is only across that road. After being fed up with changing trams on their way to school, the girls are ecstatic about it.

Who could have known then that the location would soon become our main problem? We had never given another thought to the fact that the harmless-looking building a couple of streets away was actually a jail, the kind of jail where convicts are held after their trial before being sent away to other places. Tonight there is a riot at the jail. The insecurity we have felt on the streets since Chechnya declared independence is penetrating our walls now. There are no locks or bars strong enough to make us feel safe. Right now I can hear the pounding of hundreds of feet, accompanied at regular intervals by cries of "Allah akbar! Allah akbar!" It is the *Zikr*, a ritual religious dance of the local Muslims. My sparse knowledge of this religion comes from the university course on Atheism. I only remember that the Chechens' religion is a sect, a deviation of Islam, and that the *Zikr* dance is a form of prayer. It is not the ritual dance itself that frightens me, although it must be horrifying to watch and is not supposed to be seen by strangers; it's the time and place. The fact that a bunch of convicts, supposed to be isolated from the ordinary public, are getting out of their cells to celebrate taking over the jail. What is their next step going to be? Open the gates and spread out over the nearby streets? This is certainly a most terrifying prospect.

The sixth floor would provide a good view over the three-storeyed jail, if it were not for the darkness. The figures of the dancers are invisible in the density of the night. I can only see the tongues of flame coming out of the jail yard. The riot started late in the afternoon but nothing has been mentioned on the news. I listen to both television and radio. Since the Colonel became leader of the Chechen movement for independence, Ravel's *Bolero* has been chosen to open every news release. The tense and monotonous tune sounds indifferent as if all its passion disappears in the endless repetitions.

My girls are lying quietly in their beds. Liza is ten, Alexandra is thirteen and Asya, my grandmother, is ninety.

It is hard to watch my happily organised world falling apart. To tell the truth, this is happening not for the first time in my life. But for the first time it has nothing to do with my own faults or wishes. Like a hurricane, that's what it is. Or maybe that's the wrong comparison. A hurricane is a natural disaster but what is going on now in the streets of Grozny is caused by people. The wild crowds in the two main town squares. The mocking smiles on the faces of the armed young Chechens. Their practically open slogan: "Russians out!" And we are leaving. Selling the family nests for peanuts and running for our lives to the nearby Russian cities of Stavropol, Krasnodar, anywhere, away from danger.

Somebody must take responsibility. Why did it come to this, to open terror? It is not good enough, cowering inside the doubtful safety of your house. Shut your doors and shut your mind. I was born here. I have lived here all my life. I know the troubled history of the Chechens. I think I know their character the way you come to know your next-door neighbour. I have convinced myself that if I put down on paper all the facts in their sequence, I may come to some sort of understanding. Let's start from the beginning.

I learned the history of my native place from my grandmother's stories, the stories I heard as a child. My darling *babushka* Asya became everything to me after my father's death. I was only five at the time. My beautiful young mother was looking for consolation elsewhere. *Babushka* Asya was the only one who tried to break the glass wall between myself and the rest of the world, enchanting me with endless stories of her own childhood, bringing back to life the long-lost world of the Cossack village of Kalinovskaya. That village is forever engraved in my memory: the sound-track of church bells, the contented countryside with its stables and pastures, the soft splash of salmon in the River Terek, flowing along its rocky bed to the Caspian Sea – all set against the ridge of the Caucasus mountains.

Asya's father was a priest of the local church. He had been sent to serve there after his graduation from the Seminary, a special school for Russian Orthodox priests from one of the northern regions of Russia. Kalinovskaya became home for him and his young wife. All their six children, three girls and three boys, were born there. Anastasiya, or Asya as she was called by those close to her, born in 1897, was the youngest of the girls. I can see it now: the

3

flicker of flames from the stove in the corner, a phantasm of light and shadows on the walls, created by the lamp shade, trimmed with a crochet pattern of grapes and vine leaves. I am mesmerised by my granny's soft voice. Time stops and then turns back. That was our own world and we were in our own time machine. Time and again, her stories brought that world back to life from its ashes, and the trips to her past soon became our shared pleasure and my own new reality. We ignored the sequence of events, diving into that stream of the past at any point of our own choice. In a couple of months I became a skilful swimmer, familiar with every nook and cranny of grandma Asya's memory bay.

'Tell me *babushka* (Russian for granny, with the stress on the first syllable,

please),how did you travel back home from your boarding school in Vladikavkaz?'

And the trip through time would begin. I imagined it was me, not her, wearing a green uniform with a high lace collar and a little silver pendant, neatly dressed and excited at the prospect of seeing all my family getting back together: my parents, brothers and sisters, horses and dogs, and my younger brother's cat, Vasiliy.

Grandma Asya

Goodbye, town of Vladikavkaz,
With its bright blue skies.
Goodbye, Inspector Gelikas,
With those bright blue eyes.

Inspector Gelikas was a real person and a real church boarding schools inspector. Asya had only seen him once and couldn't actually tell if he had been as handsome as the other girls believed him to be, but the contrast between his blue eyes and black hair was striking. She was singing along with the other girls. Two of them were her older sisters, Shura and Nadya. Some of the girls were sitting on high uncomfortable chairs. Others were walking up and down impatiently in pairs in the recreation hall of the boarding school. They were all waiting to be collected to go home for the Easter holidays.

Vladikavkaz was the nearest administrative and cultural centre to Grozny. The local population, Asetins, who had joined the Russian Empire voluntarily, belonged to the same Orthodox Church as the Russians. There were two secondary schools (*gimnazias*), one for girls and another for boys, a military school for boys, *Kadetskii korpus*, and a boarding school for the daughters of priests, called *Eparhkialnoe uchilische*.

Of course, they didn't have school buses then. Usually, three or four horse-drawn carriages made their way, escorted by a squad of Cossacks. The road leading through the mountains was not safe. The Cossacks protected travellers from the *abreks*, Chechen highwaymen. That was the first time I had heard the word "Chechen" mentioned in grandma Asya's stories and I needed to stop the time machine and come back to my own five-year-old self, to clear up some points.

My First Lesson on
the History of Chechnya

'Who are those people, what did they look like and where are they now, granny?'

'Oh, my dear child, they were the people who lived here long before the Russian Tsar decided to join their land to the Russian Empire.'

'And when was that, granny? What is the Russian Empire? Is it the Soviet Union?'

'Same thing, my dear, same thing. After the revolution they changed its name. The city of Grozny, where we live now, was built around the Groznaya fortress. General Ermolov ordered the fortress to be built in 1818 as the centre and main fortification for the whole Northern Caucasus. This is how they used to occupy new territories. First, they forced the local people from their land and then, if they didn't want to make room for the new Cossack settlements, they fought them and conquered them. Then they built a fortress where they posted a regular army regiment to watch and protect the new border of the Empire.'

'So the Chechens were living where we live now?'

'Yes, darling, they were. When I was born in 1897, there were Cossack villages, *stanitsas*, and Chechen villages, *auls*.'

'Were they still fighting each other?'

'No, they lived like neighbours. Sometimes they were very close, sometimes they quarrelled with each other, but they managed to create unwritten rules, a code of behaviour. Actually, their lives were very much alike.

7

They even dressed in the same way. Men, like the rest of the male population throughout the Caucasus, wore the *cherkesska* coat and a lambsfleece hat called a *papakha*. The ladies, oh! the Cossack ladies, they were immaculate and very proud of their appearance. They had to be with all the competition there! All those Chechen, Cherkessian, Georgian, even Persian, beauties the Caucasian region was so famous for! They were tall slender brunettes with a proud straight gait and soft milk-white skin without a trace of suntan. Imagine, Sonechka, the climate here was just as it is now – an average of 35°C from May till September. With their work outdoors in the fields, vineyards and orchards all day long, it wasn't easy to achieve at all. They used their own beauty recipe. They covered their faces with a mixture of sour cream and lard and wrapped them with linen scarves so that only their eyes, big and mostly brown, like those of a gazelle, were exposed. As for the clothes, again, the traditional outfit was a special Caucasian lady's "double dress", worn in such a way that the one which was worn underneath, could be seen through the splits in the front and in the sleeves. The slim long waist was bound with a leather belt embroidered with silver. So, this answers your question of what they looked like. They looked very much the same, Chechens and Cossacks.'

'And Cossacks, granny, who were they?'

'Oh, they were Russians, dear.'

'Russians?'

'Russian peasants, moved by order of the Tsar to explore the new lands, or sometimes serfs who had escaped from their brutal lords in search of a better life.'

'Please, *babushka*, go on, tell me more about it.'

This is what I remember from her stories.

Time passed, the brutal strife of the Caucasian war was over. Much blood had been shed on both sides, but the Russian army had the whole empire behind them and they won. The peace so long desired brought its own laws and some new traditions. Chechens, dwelling in their own villages, *auls*, became involved in one type of relationship or another with their Cossack neighbours. Chechens and Cossacks found a special word for their new friends and called one another *kunak* (for men) and *kunachka* (for women). *Kunachki* used to pay a visit sometimes on Sundays, to have a chat with their women-friends from the *stanitsa* over a cup of freshly brewed savoury *kalmytski* tea, taken with milk, butter and a good pinch of salt. This was a strange drink introduced by the Kalmyk tribes, Bedouin people, travelling all over the plain between the mountains with their flocks and huge herds of mostly wild horses. This tea was something I hated at first, but later I came to like it a lot and to appreciate its healing qualities. I would love to have a big bowl of it right now, with a slice of goat's cheese on toast. The Northern Caucasus was a melting pot of many cultures with its unique mixture of food, recipes, dances and fashions.

Every time someone died *kunaki* would visit their friends, bringing their condolences. I don't remember granny mentioning if Cossacks went to see their friends in the *auls*, but probably they did.

Unfortunately, not all the original population was friendly. Many of those who fought in the war became *abreks*, and made their living by robbing and often killing travellers. That is why, when travelling, the locals were recommended to ask for a Cossack escort. It was almost impossible to catch such highway robbers, because, however friendly Chechens were, their loyalty was with those of their own nationality. *Abrek* could always count on their hospitality on a rainy day. Much later, in the events I witnessed in the last years of the twentieth century, I think this kind of loyalty did the Chechens no favours.

When I think of grandma Asya's stories, vividly imprinted in my memory, the landscapes and characters look bright but flat, surreal, like those of Marc Chagall with his pre-Revolutionary Vitebsk, or of the French artist Rousseau, another master of primitivism. That is why these stories are actually asking for another genre and a special space of their own.

Vasiliy, The Talking Cat

The journey home was safe and pleasant. I was so excited that I could hardly eat when we stopped halfway for a picnic. I was sitting on a blanket with the other girls in front of all the goodies of the world, like *pirozhki* (pasties) stuffed with different vegetables, or fish, or sweet ones containing raisins and dried apricots, and many other tasty things, but no eggs, meat or poultry, because it was still Lent. One of the Cossacks was helping two ladies, mothers of my classmates, with the samovar.

Normally our parents took the trips from school in turns with the parents of the other children who lived in the neighbourhood. All of them belonged to the clergy like my father, and their wives, apart from having a number of children, up to ten or more, had their own social duties, helping and advising the village women. I remember my mother was always busy taking part herself in every chore about the house, although we had the help of a woman who cooked the meals and another one, coming once a week to clean, and a nanny who helped with the children. All of them shared the table with us at mealtimes, bringing news from the village and stories about their own families and friends.

I was so excited at the prospect of seeing everyone again, because it was my first year away from home. My two older sisters and the other girls, their close friends who were well known to me, were at the same school, but I missed my younger brother Mitya very much. We were the youngest children in the family and were very close, like twins. Now I was sitting in the carriage. The warm spring sun, the voices of my friends singing a sad, monotonous song about a hermit and his hardships, *"Po dikim stepyam Zabaikalya"*, and the sound of horses' hooves on the road made me slip into a contented doze and miss the exact moment of the family reunion. I could hardly remember my father's strong arms lifting me up. I was enveloped by the familiar fresh fragrance of incense from the wide sleeves of his *ryasa*, a black gown worn by Russian priests.

The next day, as soon as I opened my eyes, a wave of familiar sounds and smells filled me with such complete happiness as the one we are blessed to experience only in our early childhood. I was sharing the bedroom with my two sisters, and realised that it must be very early because they were both still sound asleep after the day-long journey and a welcome-home party, which, as was now clear, I had sadly missed. Suddenly I felt so left out and betrayed by everyone, that the tears were ready to stream down my cheeks, when I saw the door handle gently move and the two brown eyes and richly freckled snub nose of my beloved brother Mitya peep round the door. He made a sign that he would be waiting for me outside and I quickly sneaked out of the bedroom, with a big knitted woollen shawl wrapped round my shoulders.

One look at Mitya's face told me that he had another terrible secret to share with me. He had probably forgotten that I was a grown-up, no-nonsense schoolgirl now.

'Hello, Mitya, what's wrong?'

'Asya, my cat Vasiliy is talking!'

'What do you mean, talking? Is he meowing?'

'No, he's talking like you and me! With a rather husky voice!'

'You are a silly boy, cats don't talk. Where is he anyway?'

'He's in the summer kitchen. I wanted to take him fishing with me, started calling him and he answered me in plain Russian. Amazing! We could be famous if we invited the scientists to do research on him.'

'Let me see him! Now!'

I was intrigued now, too. We crossed the yard and approached the doors of our so-called summer kitchen, a separately built one-room house, equipped with a big *pechka*, a Russian stove, which would have been too hot to use in the house kitchen during the summertime. The summer kitchen was quite large and even had some sleeping accommodation which was very much appreciated by our cats. We stopped at the kitchen door and Mitya called:

'Vasiliy!'

'What?' The answer from the darkness of the room came in a thick manly bass.

Mitya looked at me victoriously. 'Now you see!'

'Vasiliy!' he called again.

'What?' answered the cat.

Goodness me!

'Mitya we must get him and wake everyone up. Come on, let's do it.'

We took a cautious first step, holding hands tightly.

'Vasiliy!' we called together, taking another step.

'What?' the same voice asked us, and we could see now the bulky figure of a man stretched on the bench.

'Who are *you*?' we shouted in chorus.

'I'm Vasiliy, His Honour Officer Mikhail Gruzdov's new *denschik*. I've just arrived. I didn't want to wake everyone and decided to wait here.'

So that explained the miraculous talking cat, Vasiliy. A *denschik* was a special Cossack soldier assigned to every Cossack officer as a batman, something in between a butler and a scullery maid.

But not every miracle could have been explained so easily.

And here is another of *babushka* Asya's stories:

How I Saw a Real Witch

When I was seven years old, I was small in height, but stubborn out of all proportion. My favourite saying was: "Whatever you say, my answer is *nyet*". It was my first school summer holiday, and the fact that I was a schoolgirl now contributed even more to my spirit of independence. My older sister Nadya, who had the most refined tastes in the family, called me a future suffragette. She was about to start teaching at a school in Grozny, and her main concern was the latest Paris fashions and the choice between two captains, the Cossack or the regular ground force one. But even my middle sister Shura, the kindest and sweetest person in the world, often admitted that I would get myself into trouble one day. And so I did.

It was the end of the summer. My sisters and I used to go for a swim in the Terek at sunset, when the sand on the beach was still very hot, but the fresh breeze from the mountains promised a much desired coolness. We were probably three or four houses away from home and were passing a lonely bench under an apricot tree in the middle of the street when I suddenly decided that I wanted to stop there for a while. Neither Shura's concern nor Nadya's scorn could move me from the place.

'I'm staying here. Whatever you say, my answer is *nyet*.'

'You are a silly little brat! Just you wait! Don't you know there's a witch in the village? She lives in the old abandoned house at the end of the street. She will get you, just you wait and see!' said Nadya.

But I didn't want to hear. My sisters left me alone. I was sitting on the bench, not very happy with myself, imagining everyone at home getting together for supper round the big family table in the summer kitchen, and Frosya, the kitchen maid, putting on the samovar. The girls would have changed into their white cotton dresses by now, father would be about to come home from the church, my older brother Misha would be back from the mountains and showing his hunting trophies and Mitya would be helping mother to lay the table. I would have been happy to join them but I needed to keep my word.

In the meantime it was getting darker and a sudden gust of wind along the street made me shiver with an unpleasant feeling of something nasty approaching. I looked down to the far end of the street only to see the silhouette of a woman walking in my direction. Suddenly I saw her jump and turn into a wheel, a big dark wooden wheel, rolling towards me! I sat frozen on my bench and the next thing I saw was the wheel turning into a big black cat and leaping with its stretched paws towards me. I jumped from the bench with a wild cry and ran as fast as I could until I heard my father's voice calling me and I felt him take hold of my sweaty hand. At home I made Mitya jealous because I had seen the witch and he hadn't. Father said it was my fear that I had seen. And mother told all three of us sisters that she was not pleased with us, and tomorrow nobody would be allowed to go for a swim. I was sent to bed straight after supper, and went to sleep, crying because no one understood me. And it was their loss that they didn't believe me about the witch. Next time she appeared I would be ready and I would protect them all like the girl-warrior, Joan of Arc.

Summer Life. The Ducks
and their Mysterious Disease

Every summer my parents' house was full of young people:
the friends and schoolmates of my brothers and sisters,
young distant relatives or the children of my parents'
friends. It was considered possible and even healthy for
the younger generation to mix with one another under
the wise and discreet supervision of the grown-ups. My
sisters, brothers and I in our turn were allowed to stay at
our friends' houses whenever we were invited, provided
that our parents had met before.

Everyone took part in the everyday household routine.
Nevertheless, plenty of time was left for sports, picnics
and other entertainments. One of these, particularly loved
by everyone, was swimming in the river. We had specially
fenced areas in the river for young children and girls, and
all the rest was for the young men. Girls and boys wore
their mothers' old cotton summer dresses for swimming,
which was an everlasting source of jokes, because
my brothers used to steal mother's caps and scarves
to complete their outfits. The other favourite outdoor
occupations were fishing and hunting, as well as massive
picnics with starched tablecloths and samovars.

There were hot, fragrant summer nights, very dark in
this part of the world, "with stars scattered across the
black velvet of the sky like diamonds". The quotation is
from a "romance", a kind of love song extremely popular
in Russia. The nights were full of music and romance.
Misha played the guitar. His *denschik*, Vasiliy, when
he was not chasing some village beauty, would bring

out his *garmoshka*, a smaller version of the accordion. Mitya learned to play the balalaika from his friends in the village. My middle brother, Georgiy, had a pleasant baritone voice. I was not bad myself. My father called me his "silver bell". But the best of all was Shura's mezzo-soprano. We were all taught to sing in a choir, and our repertoire included everything from folksongs to opera.

Shura and I were very excited when we were allowed to use a newly built barn as an extra dining room. Now we could organise proper concerts and performances! Nadya was expecting visitors that summer, so she came down to us humble people and decorated the place with flower arrangements and curtains. Shura took a big piece of cardboard and wrote with a whitewash brush in her best French: *La Cantine*. The board was solemnly attached over the barn door and stayed there intact till the end of the week. The barn was found useful by all members of the family. Fresh air and lots of outdoor activities gave the young people healthy appetites. The heaps of food consumed in *La Cantine* three times a day provoked my brothers by the end of the week to change the sign to *Le Cochon* using the same brush. *Le Cochon* means "The Pig". Within a few days, to Nadya's fierce disapproval, the shed was downgraded to simply *Obzhorka*, which means "Piggery".

Not all the jokes were harmless. One afternoon the whole sleepy household was alarmed by the maid Frosya's terrifying shriek from the poultry yard behind the garden. Mother ran towards her followed by Mitya and myself, her "tails" as she called us. Goodness gracious! What had happened to our ducks? They all seemed to be stricken by some strange disease. They could hardly walk, were very wobbly and totally disorientated. There were a couple of dozen of them altogether. Mother forbade us to approach any of them. She put on her garden gloves and examined some of those that already seemed to be dead. But they were not! They were warm and breathing, so it might be a case of lethargy then. In the meantime Frosya checked the trough and was surprised by the smell of the remnants of the ducks' food in it. It smelled unmistakably of vodka. At that moment we saw our teenage brother Georgiy, or Zhora as everyone called him, hiding behind the fence, struggling with laughter. Now you can guess what kind of disease our ducks had caught. Mother was very angry with Zhora and locked him in his room till night.

We spent the rest of the afternoon watching the poor drunken birds, keeping them out of the sun and splashing water on them. Luckily for Zhora, all the ducks were well before dark, and he got back his freedom with a very serious threat from mother that he would be beaten if he tried something as bad as that again. She always promised us a good spanking when we misbehaved, but I don't remember any one of us ever having been touched with a belt or willow stick, as sometimes happened with children from other families.

Zhora's sense of adventure brought him later in his life to the revolutionary party of the Cadets, Constitutional Democrats. This happened in about 1915, when he was in the army.

I remember the time of the first serious disagreement in the family when Zhora came back home for the summer vacation, declaring that he was leaving the seminary, because God did not exist and that Charles Darwin's "Theory of Evolution of Species" showed it quite clearly. After that there was no room for us in *Le Cochon* between meals, because Zhora and father, the priest who had devoted his life to the church, stayed there after meals fiercely discussing the matter. By the end of that summer it was agreed that Zhora would try the teaching profession. But the First World War interfered with this plan as it did with many others. Zhora joined the army as a volunteer.

All these and many other unfortunate events happened nine years later, in 1914, and in the meantime we were all happy and our life was shielded from the rest of the cruel world by our parents' love and kindness.

The First Wartime Dance

When the First World War started I was in my last year at the boarding school. The school gave us the necessary knowledge and a certificate to qualify us as elementary school teachers, and we were all looking forward to starting our grown-up life. I knew already that I was going to take a position in one of the schools in Vladikavkaz. Some girls had already become engaged and were looking at the world with hazy eyes, reminding me of the cows in the summer meadow. Having started school a year earlier than most of my classmates, I was only sixteen. I was full of energy and found it difficult to behave in a grown-up way. I was lucky to be bony and small, otherwise the Principal would have ordered me to wear a corset, as she did with all the plump girls in our class.

The Principal was a remarkable woman, well connected in high society, the spinster sister of someone important, and looked like a picture from a fashion magazine: always laced up tightly at her waist and hips with her hair shaped round her face in a high wave. She was short sighted and used a monocle which hung on a gold chain round her neck. We did not see much of her, but once in a while she used to ask the teachers to line us up for an inspection. After scrupulous examination through that monocle, she would point with it to the object in need of improvement with the words: 'Corset. Another corset. Hair brushed properly. Sleeves too long. This dress is too short. And another corset.' In ten years at school I probably saw her about ten times. We did not like or dislike her. We were sure she was the way she should be. I now think that, together with the teacher of Good Manners and Dancing, she did a good job, making young ladies out of the clumsy country girls we had been. Her dry, matter-of-fact manner was broken just once in all the years I knew her.

I received a letter from home, saying that Zhora had joined the army voluntarily and was about to be sent to the front. One Sunday morning I was told that my brothers had come to visit me and I was allowed to see them for about an hour in the recreation hall. Generally we were not allowed to leave the school during the term. When I came downstairs I saw Zhora and five other young men I had never met before. All of them were wearing army uniforms. Zhora winked at me and started talking about things at home while the teacher was watching us, but as soon as she left he introduced his new friends, volunteers like himself. He told me that they had a whole day's leave before being sent to the front and asked if I could call the girls, my classmates, to join us.

The girls slipped downstairs with me and everyone was introduced to each other. After half an hour of conversation, one of the young men went up to the grand piano in the corner of the hall and started softly trying the keys. He turned out to be good with popular melodies and tunes. Everyone thought that a little bit of dancing would be a lovely idea. But how could we make it so quiet that the teacher upstairs wouldn't hear us? I gave everyone a hint by taking my shoes off. The next moment all our shoes were in a line along the wall. And a strangely silent dancing party began.

Of course we could not keep it quiet all the time. In the middle of the most energetic polka, the heavy doors opened and the Principal herself entered the hall. Everyone froze.

'What is going on here? Can anyone explain it to me?'

I took a step forward.

'Please allow me to introduce my brothers, Principal. They're visiting me before going to the front tomorrow'.

The Principal looked at me for a second and I realised that her short-sighted eyes were not only wonderfully green, but also bright because they were close to tears.

'You may continue', she said. 'And put your shoes back on, please.'

The Revolution

My older sister Nadya took me to the "Paris Fashions" dressmaker's shop, the best one in Vladikavkaz, where I was measured in the presence of Madame herself. No wonder, considering we were going to order my first full grown-up wardrobe. We spent the whole morning choosing the styles and fabrics, took a sample of each, and after a break for tea and *pirozhki* at the café across the road, went to order matching shoes and hats.

For me the Revolution started when the ladies stopped wearing hats. At first hats were replaced voluntarily by red scarves. The latter were worn as a special declaration of the new ideas by the girls who joined in the anti-war and anti-government demonstrations. Later, after the October Revolution, it was dangerous to wear hats, because everyone whose background had been different from a working class or peasant one was considered to be an enemy.

All these and many other strange and cruel things happened three years later, but in the meantime I enjoyed my new status as a lady of independent means. I also loved visiting my parents in Kalinovskaya. Shortly before the war there was a period when they were almost on their own. Misha, the eldest, the Cossack regiment's officer, married Lyudmila, the daughter of a Cossack farmer. She had been an apprentice in a fashion dress workshop in Grozny. Their wedding was a big family event, and the newly-weds, after a honeymoon trip to Saint-Petersburg, settled in Grozny, where Misha's regiment was posted. Shura's wedding was the next one. She married Konstantin, the son of old friends of the family. He was a regular army officer. And the fact that they also lived in Vladikavkaz helped me to enjoy my independence. Nadya lived in Grozny. She was still unmarried, by her own choice. She considered that being a young and attractive woman was a full-time occupation and she had never liked housekeeping. Her work as a teacher was mainly an excuse to escape country life. There were also rumours that she had met a new friend at one of the city Easter balls. He was a foreigner, an employee of a new British Oil Company, which had recently been established in Chechnya, but she was very discreet about him.

Grozny was an expanding place with all the benefits of city life, attracting the attention of businessmen and specialists when serious development of the local oil wells began.

Mitya was in Moscow. His visits disturbed our ordinary but pleasant existence, introducing an atmosphere of instability and making its simplicity seem shallow and its pleasures false. He was the first to tell us about Rasputin. The Empire was full of rumours of moral degradation in high society. He said that the rumours about Rasputin and his role in the court had ruined Tsaritsa Alexandra's reputation.

This time we were all back home for the Christmas and New Year celebrations. Again there were political disputes between Mitya and papa. 'The Russian people's fundamental belief was a faith in a good Father-Tsar. Wasn't the power of tsars blessed by God?' I didn't dare to express my views. Probably I hardly had any. One moment I totally agreed with papa, that everything had to stay as it was, because "a poor peace is better than a rich war", the next moment I thought Mitya was right: we deserved better rulers.

As for the war, it was going on and on. After meeting Mitya, returning to Vladikavkaz and taking part in anti-war demonstrations with fellow-teachers was a natural and logical step. The most enjoyable part of the demonstrations for me was singing in chorus. The tunes of the revolutionary songs were so beautiful, the words about freedom and happiness so sincere! I was singing and tears blurred my vision. I wanted my brothers to come back home from the war. I wanted the workers to have a better life. I personally did not know any workers, and the peasants in our village were all well-off. There were occasional hiccups with drunkards, but the majority were hard-working and doing well. That is why they were all sent to Siberia as *kulaki* in the 1920s. But that is another story.

In the meantime, I greeted the February Revolution of 1917 with the hope of seeing my brothers back home soon. But in reality that year the old house gave us its shelter and support for the last time. Spring was taking over slowly. The roads were a muddy disaster. Shura with her baby son Igor and I were the only passengers daring to hire a carriage at that time of year. I was praying silently all the way. 'Please, dear God, let us get there safely.' Everything was going to be fine again. Father and mother would look after us till the end of the war, when the young men would return and take their wives and children home. Lyudmila with her son Boris was already in Kalinovskaya and she was pregnant with her second child. When Misha came home from the war a new baby would probably already be born.

God helped us on that occasion and we arrived without breakdown before dark. My heart sank when I saw my mother's face stricken with grief.

'Misha or Zhora?' I asked straight away.

It was Misha. A Cossack messenger had brought the letter that very day. Killed in action. Two weeks later another message was sent to inform us that Zhora had been lost in battle. As for Mitya, all we knew was that he had joined the revolutionary forces somewhere.

I do not know how we would have managed to live through those times if it had not been for the babies who constantly demanded our attention and care. By the end of the month there were three of them altogether. Lyudmila gave birth to a girl prematurely. The christening took place soon after Misha's funeral. The baby was named Alevtina, which in the household was quickly turned into Alusya or Lusya. She was a little miracle who survived in spite of the midwife's grave predictions and a lack of mother's milk. Those three little creatures Igor, Boris and Alusya became the light and hope of our existence.

The cellar was still full of good home-produced food. Although not much of an eater myself, I enjoyed going down there and taking a look at the sacks of wheat flour, dried beans and peas, and the barrel of honey. Another compartment was full of boxes of sand containing root vegetables and potatoes. Such visits gave me some reassurance. 'At least we have enough food for mothers and children to survive till the next harvest. We still have a cow, some goats and poultry.' I opened the small door leading into the deepest part of the cellar where on a piece of slowly melting ice, brought from the forest at the end of the winter, stood cheerful rows of jars of cream, butter and cottage cheese. They filled my heart with pride in a job well done. I was working on the milk separator that day and helping Frosya in the kitchen.

Father was very busy at church. It was a sad time of

many funeral services, but he tried to give his people all the hope he could. Shura and I were singing in the choir every day now, and the village people liked the way our strong, young voices blended together. Some of them asked us if we could come and sing at occasional wartime weddings. Sometimes they even tried to pay us, but later, knowing that we refused to take money, used to bring baskets of goodies "for the little ones" as they used to say: sweets, cakes, sugared fruit. Little did we know that in a while, our amateur performances would become our only source of income. But that would happen later, the following year.

Amazing that the main concern of our mother at that time was her grandchildren's poor appetites.

An Appetite Purse

The two boys Igor and Boris were lazy eaters, for different reasons. Igor was too occupied with the life going on around him and from the moment he started to talk he had never stopped asking questions. He simply could not spare his mouth for eating. Boris, on the contrary, was a boy of very few words, absorbed with his inner world. He could freeze with a mouthful of porridge for half an hour. My mother's views on bringing up her grandchildren had probably changed since we were babies. She decided that she had to make the boys eat. The best way of encouraging an appetite was to have your meal in good company.

Our next door neighbour, Maria Semyonovna, or just Semyonovna as everyone in the village called her, using her patronymic, was a widow with two sons, who never had any problem with their appetites. She was the funniest person I had ever known in my whole life, full of jokes, stories and little folk songs, *chastushki*. Nowadays she would probably have been a famous comedian. So my mother and Semyonovna had a special routine for inviting them all for breakfast. Normally meals were served in the kitchen and as soon as the food was ready, my mother used to come up to the low willow fence between the two gardens and shout, 'Semyonovna, are you coming?' Semyonovna would shout back, 'Coming, coming!'

'Are you bringing "the appetite" with you?'

'I am, I am.'

The next moment Semyonovna and her two boys were taking their places at the table opposite our problem eaters. Semyonovna was carrying a handmade and richly embroidered red velvet purse, which was supposed to be "an appetite" itself. Both boys were totally convinced that the presence of the magic purse made their food taste marvellous. In went the porridge into their wide open mouths accompanied by the rhythms of Semyonovna's *chastushki*. When she was busy and asked us to excuse her and her sons, she would always lend us her "appetite purse", but only for the current meal, because she definitely needed it in her household every day.

Barley Coffee

The morning the first squad of Reds appeared in the doorway of our kitchen, Semyonovna had made us all laugh by telling the story of how she had been frightened by the scarecrow in the cornfield behind the house. It seemed to be moving on its own. And then she realised it was a pig trying to dig something out from underneath it. It was nice to forget our troubles for a while and share a good laugh. We had started to feel some shortages. It was impossible to buy real coffee, so we milled freshly roasted barley instead and brewed it as we normally did with coffee. With the addition of sugar and cream the result was fantastic. Everyone was enjoying a second cup. The kitchen smelled very homely of roasted barley and freshly baked bread.

And then the door opened and let the war itself step in. The men with red bands across the fronts of their hats looked very tired and were covered with dust from the road. My father was in the church, so there were only women and children around the table. Unfortunately, they were women whose sons, brothers and husbands were on the opposite side of the front line to the newcomers. We were all fully aware of the danger.

'Is this the house of the priest?' the question followed.

Another danger. Priests were illegal under the Bolsheviks. Religion had already been proclaimed "an opium for the people" and the church, as an institution, had been separated from the state.

'Yes, it is,' answered my mother quickly. 'Please come on in and have something to eat. Come on, girls, take the little ones out. They have finished their meal anyway'.

With this most simple gesture of hospitality my mother saved us all for the time being. The men stopped being soldiers and became just men, tired and hungry.

'What is it that smells so nice, mother?' asked one of them, addressing my mother in a way usual for an ordinary young man.

'It's our barley coffee, son,' she answered him in the same way. 'Have a cup, please.'

The next moment there was a cup of the hot aromatic drink and a thick slice of warm bread spread with butter and covered with cottage cheese in front of every man. I poured cream into their cups trying to keep my shaky hands steady. This time we were lucky. There were only five of them; the rest of the regiment had settled in the village school. They asked my mother if she could cook for them, and she eagerly agreed, knowing she was buying time for us all. The Reds filled our backyard with calves and sheep destined to become their food in the near future. Our beloved *Le Cochon* now became an army canteen, but we were glad. The soldiers were happy with their food and pleased with our hospitality. They closed the church, taking every valuable piece of silver, like the icon frames and crosses, and a gold communion cup into a "revolutionary treasury", but father, after spending a night under arrest in the school cellar, was let alone.

For me that was a night of awareness. I could not sleep and went out with Misha's two hunting dogs following me everywhere. I walked along the quiet street of my lovely Kalinovskaya, pausing at the bench where as a child I saw the witch rolling by. I was thinking that in times of real danger I had to be my family's support and hope. I was only twenty years old.

Escape

During the next months political power in the village changed several times. Apart from the two opposing fighting parties, the Reds – Bolsheviks – and the Whites, who were the supporters of the monarchy, there were multicoloured bands of vagabonds proclaiming themselves to be the revolutionary force based on their own beliefs. The final victory of the Bolsheviks, who had lately renamed themselves Communists, came with the appointment of the new local government, whose primary goal was to identify and punish "strange elements". My father was taken for investigation and sent to a labour camp in the north west of Russia. Our house was taken from us into the "revolutionary treasury". We were not even allowed to keep our clothes, but were happy to escape alive. My sister Shura and my sister-in-law Lyudmila had spent the night before standing in the garden trembling in their nightdresses. Facing the guns pointed at them, they were silently saying goodbye to their children and to life itself. The Reds wanted to know if they collected money to help the Whites and if they did not, who in the village did. They denied both. God knows why, but they let them go in the end.

So now there we were, a caravan of pilgrims: my mother, Lyudmila with two young children, Boris and Alusya, Shura with her son Igor and me. We were walking along the road carrying the children, the only treasure we really cared for. Nothing was important but the safety of these little creatures. We headed to Grozny hoping to join Nadya and find a new life for us all.

Sofia's Comments

I could never get from my grandmother the whole picture of their escape and forced trek to Grozny. She said they were lucky to get a lift from time to time. Mostly there was enough room on the peasant cart only for the oldest and the youngest ones. By the time they reached the outskirts of the town, everyone was exhausted. Only Igor kept asking questions, mainly addressing Asya because nobody else could concentrate on answering.

All that happened to them later in Grozny sounded obscure and vague. They could not find teaching jobs, because employment of anyone with their kind of social background was prohibited by the new government. For several months their only source of living was singing in the only church officially allowed to exist in Grozny. This was the church where first I and then both my daughters were later to be secretly christened, the Archangel Michael Church located in our street, literally next door. That church was destroyed in the Chechen war of 2000 but restored after the war ended.

So they sang in the church and were paid with food and sometimes with a rouble or two. Nadya had to move out of her fine apartment. They were all sharing a rented room and a kitchen on credit. After keeping the children safe and sound, the family's next concern was to make contact with father in the labour camp. Things improved when some clever people advised them to hide their background by entering the word "service" when filling in application forms. It helped, and soon Asya and then Shura returned to teaching. Lyudmila stayed at home looking after the children and taking rare orders for dressmaking. They started writing letters to the authorities, trying to get some information about their father. It was an enormous relief to receive an answer at last, saying that he was alive and held in a labour camp on Lake Ladoga. Now they started another round of letter-writing, asking for permission to visit him.

In the meantime, after being dismissed from several different schools as soon as the trick with the "service" was discovered, Anastasiya took a teaching position in the First Chechen School in Grozny. Most of her pupils were grown-up men vigorously twisting their tongues in their effort to learn to read Russian, a language, which was not quite familiar to them in its colloquial form. Anastasiya sincerely sympathised with her students and tried to help them in every possible way.

And there was another area where teacher and students found mutual understanding. It was in their attitude to religion. Officially, everyone in the school was expected to support atheism, the religion of the new political power. There were special studies and demonstrations to prove that God had never existed. Any other points of view were considered to be harmful and were subject to punishment. But sometimes at noon a teacher coming into the classroom would see some of his Muslim students sitting on their desks facing East and saying their prayers. When Anastasiya happened to find herself in a situation like this she would discreetly step back, close the door and wait outside until they had finished. After that she would begin her lesson in the ordinary way. Her understanding made her the most popular figure among the students. Their mutual conspiracy helped her in her everyday work. By the end of the first year her pupils could speak Russian, as well as read and write, and had also made good progress in their maths and natural science studies. Her general opinion of the Chechens as scholars was always very high.

A Strange Visitor

Now I suppose it is time for me to return to the events of my own childhood. My first encounter with a Chechen happened on a bright day in spring 1959. It was Sunday. I was allowed at last to go for a walk after breakfast and washing up. Our backyard, white with cherry blossom, was full of sunshine and the hum of bees. I saw him as soon as I went out into the yard. There he was, the stranger, a rather unusual looking old man. I had never seen anyone like him before. There was an air of distinction and self-sufficiency about him. He was old and oddly dressed in a long cotton jacket and tall lamb's fleece hat. I came up closer. He looked at me, and something much bigger than me, bigger than this yard and this street, reflected in his eyes. Granny was the only one who dared to approach him. The rest of the curious neighbourhood was watching the whole scene from behind their curtains. Granny greeted the stranger, asked him where he was from and sent me for a glass of water for him. The stranger smiled at granny as if he recognised somebody of his own status and answered that he was from what is known as Kazakhstan now, but that more than seventy years ago he had built this house for his family and had lived here.

The house where we lived belonged to the council, as did every big house in the USSR. It was divided into five flats. We had lived in number five since I was six. That was the place where I was both happy and unhappy in so many different ways. It was my home and then my daughters' home, too. Now I think I should have thanked that man, for having built such a good and spacious house, with high ceilings and tall windows. The windows had wooden shutters attached to them, and the window sills were so wide you could sit on them on hot summer nights with the lights off, watching the sky, listening to the radio, or just dreaming in silence broken only by the song of crickets. It was also a good place for writing poetry, which was effortlessly streaming out of me on to paper, or rather descending to me from the mysterious vastness of the night sky.

Granny left the old man to his own memories and returned to her daily routine. I followed her and heard a terrifying story of what had been done to two whole nations by the powerful evil of Stalin's regime. In 1943 the two nations, Chechens and Ingush, who lived closely together, sharing in many ways their religion, customs and language, were overnight moved out from the places where they had lived for centuries, put on to trains and forcibly evacuated to the Kazahkstan steppes. Officially the reason for this act of total brutality was that some individuals of these nationalities had received Nazi parachutists in the mountains. It was the first time I had heard about this. I was nine at the time. I do not know how the grown-ups could have totally avoided the subject for all those years, but they did. It was fear that kept their lips sealed.

Now Stalin's epoch of blood had ended and Khrushchev was in the Kremlin. All the victims of the regime were being released from their jails and camps in the faraway corners of the Soviet Union. No, not all of them, only those who survived. Granny told me that now, thank God, those times were over. Nikita Khrushchev and the new Soviet government were letting Chechens and Ingush come back to their native land.

That year when we returned to school in September after the summer holidays, the first Chechen children joined us in our classes. The first boy to appear in our class was introduced to us by his first name, Salautdin, but he asked to be called by a Russian name, Slava. Soon after that, Chechen children were in every class, and each of them had two names: one was for official papers, sounding unusual to a Russian ear, the other one was a plain Russian name. Muhammed called himself Misha, Zula was Zena and so on. I suppose they were as well received in the class as any other child would be. At the end of the same year another Chechen boy joined our class. He seemed to be more distant from the other children, but nobody really paid attention to that. Once, in the drawing lesson, when everyone was busy reproducing a composition of a clay bowl with some onions in it, I overheard the newcomer talking to Slava behind me. He asked him why he mixed with Russian boys, told him that all Russians were enemies, and that sooner or later they would be avenged for all they had done to Chechens. That was when I first started to realise how hated we were by those people. I wanted to shout to him, 'We didn't do that to you. Stalin's system punished everyone without exception.' But my family had stayed here while his was exiled, that was what mattered to him.

The Hatred

It is a strange feeling to know that someone hates you so much they would do anything to humiliate you or would even kill you. Now in 1991 a long-forgotten childhood revelation came back to me. As if the brew of blood spilt over the centuries and kept under control by the System was coming to the boil and, once it boiled over, there would be no place for mercy in this world any more.

It all started in 1957 when the Chechens were allowed to return home to the places where they had lived before the exile. Their former houses were occupied by people from Ukraine and the South of Russia. In practically the same way, these people had been forcibly moved to Chechnya, replacing the former population. They had lived in their new settlements for about fifteen years by then. There had been years of hardship both during and after the war. They had planted new gardens and ploughed new fields. The land christened with their sweat had become their land. The old ones were put to rest in that land and children were born there.

Now they were being told by the former owners to leave or ... anything might happen to them if they did not. The former owners offered to buy property back from the new occupants, but the price had to be named by the buyers. There were rumours that someone had refused to leave and the whole family had been killed the following night. Panic started to spread. The local authorities pretended not to know anything about it. First the *auls* were cleared, and then the Chechens started establishing themselves in the *stanitsas* too. The balance that had existed before the exile was broken. They hated us Russians, and lusted for revenge.

In the meantime, Groznenskaya Oblast was renamed Chechen-Ingush Autonomous Soviet Socialist Republic, ChIASSR, or Checheno-Ingushetiya. It was incorporated, like the rest of the small republics of the Northern Caucasus, into the Russian Federal Soviet Socialist Republic, the biggest of the fifteen Federal Republics of the USSR. Chechens and Ingush could benefit from the privileges granted to small nations in the Soviet Union. For instance, there was a special quota for higher education. Soon there was a big change in the cultural life of Grozny. A new Chechen drama theatre opened. Folk singing and dancing groups appeared in the programmes of the local Philharmonia. The fine arts museum held exhibitions of Chechen artists. It became obvious that everyone, whatever their nationality, only gained from sharing their cultural inheritance.

But in spite of all that, the darker side of the relationship between the two groups of the population continued to exist. Every day there was the realization that they were different. It was as if they were only pretending to be loyal citizens - in fact there was a much stronger law under which they lived behind closed doors.

Once I was very surprised when, taking a tram to the city market with my granny, I noticed that Chechen women would suddenly stand up when a man got on to the tram. It was equally strange to see a small procession consisting of a man in his tall woollen hat proudly walking along the street followed by a woman, or sometimes two women, bent to the ground under a heavy sack or bag. And one would never see a Chechen man carrying a baby. My grandmother knew the reason. She told me this behaviour was attributed to *Shariat*, a book of rules, or "laws" as they called them. The book was probably as old as our *Domostroy*. Strangely enough they were still following their medieval constitution. She also told me to stop staring because it was not polite, considering it was none of our business whatsoever.

As I understand now, Chechens had always lived like that, but before the Revolution nobody forced them to pretend otherwise. In contrast, the communist regime was focused on controlling not only public life but also people's private life. The whole nation had found a way of dealing with this and surprisingly it had been what an individual would do: pretend and live a double life. Be loyal, learn and repeat all the proper words and you would be left to your own devices. Then you could live your life according to *Shariat* rules and be respected by the other, much greater, authority of your Muslim community. Psychiatrists say a double life destroys one's personality. What if this were applicable to a whole nation?

Most of the local Russian-speaking population, especially those who arrived after 1943 as a replacement, knew nothing at all about these ethnic and religious differences, and in any case, in the Soviet Union religion had been officially banned. Not everyone had a grandmother to tell them not to stare or to stop laughing at the odd ways of different people.

A real problem arose when you met a Chechen who behaved just like anyone else. This did not mean that there was not another side to him. A Russian girl would believe she had found true love and commitment only to realise eventually that she would never be accepted by his family. Does this happen everywhere in the world where communities of different faiths live closely together? The strict *Shariat* rules did not allow young Chechen girls and boys to go out together and so Chechens started chasing Russian girls, especially the teenagers. The girls were instructed by their terrified parents never to talk to strangers. And the old fairy tale of Red Riding Hood and the wicked wolf was told and re-told in my beautiful green town..... .

The hostility between the two groups of the population grew. It culminated in a demonstration of local Russians against the Chechens in 1958. My grandparents and I missed it, having been on holiday on the Caspian Sea.

Sofia finished typing the last passage and stood up from her PC in the corner of a one-roomed legal office. A fine old house in one of the crooked lanes of old Moscow had been converted into a rabbit warren of tiny offices. It was nine o'clock, the office had closed long ago. Recently she had resumed her writing about Chechnya. It was not easy sitting there late at night after a hard day's work. It was painful trying to recover the events of the past year and their degrading consequences. Her reflections on aspects of daily life in Grozny, and in particular the attitude there to Russian girls, had brought back the most terrible moments of her life, everything that had happened to Alexandra.

She was sitting looking through a dozen pages, the beginning of the book she had started writing the night when violence became inevitable. Those first pages were retyped and followed by new ones describing the events of the nineteenth century. She was keeping the promise she had made to herself that night in May 1991 to make an attempt at understanding the roots of the trouble in Chechnya. The easiest way would be to blame the Chechens, their wild revengeful medieval nature, the way they let their manipulative leaders exploit their religious and national feelings, but this would not be the answer. She considered herself capable of a deeper analysis of the situation. The closer she came in her story to the present time, the more difficult it was to remain disengaged. She was not happy with the "Hatred" chapter at all. The whole concept seemed wrong. The best thing to do was to leave it aside for a while.

She had another reason for coming back to her writing,

apart from sorting out her own thoughts. There was someone in her life, more a ghost, a phantom now, than a real person, a man. She wanted to keep a record for his sake, too.

'I've become a robot. Mark would not recognise me.'

Sofia had felt that for some time now that she was doing the things she had to do automatically, checking every step, like climbing a mountain: right foot, left foot, check the rope, up and up, and up. This was her way of coping, her self-control program that had never let her down so far.

She was standing in front of the mirror taking her lipstick out of her bag before locking up the office and heading for home. She paused, critically surveying her reflection. Had she changed a lot? She was wearing shoulder-length hair now to save on hairdresser's bills. Her cheekbones looked sharper. 'It's because I've lost weight. What a waste of clothes! Grey hair. Far too much for a forty-year-old. Time to do the roots. Nobody would guess with colouring.' The main change was inside, and that change was showing in the intense look of her green eyes, in the new dry line of her lips which once were naturally full and always ready to smile.

Her expression softened when she thought of Mark. He had been a good listener. It was a shame they had not had enough time to talk. Having visited the country when the political system was changing was a unique experience for him.

'How did it actually happen, step by step, in the economy? Did you feel the difference?'

'Lucky you,' Sofia replied. 'Here, you see a guinea pig of *perestroika*, Mark. I've experienced every new structure.'

45

This was the remedy for her writer's block. She would drop the subject of the Chechen war for the time being and start a new chapter of less painful reminiscences.

In the Whirlwind of Perestroika

For me, a teacher of English and translator, and for many other people like myself, professionally linked to foreign languages, Gorbachev's *perestroika* brought first and foremost the opportunity to join the rest of the world. Speaking from a more selfish point of view, it was a chance to make some money for a change. During the fifteen years since I had graduated from the University my work had been strictly confined to written translation. Now, at last, I could try some live interpreting. It had been frightening at the beginning, but my first assignments were with the local government departments responsible for welcoming foreign delegations, and turned out to be just an exchange of pleasantries. I realised then that I had made the right choice in studying English. The delegations were from all over the world: Asian and Arabic countries, Western Europe. They all spoke English, or rather an international communication jargon based on English vocabulary and grammar, and I soon became fluent in this.

It was exciting meeting people of different cultural backgrounds. They did not know much about life in the Soviet Union. It was a fair exchange: they took back home lots of curious information and I accumulated a collection of stories from my new job which I used to entertain my friends. There was the time when I had been interpreting for a delegation from Jordan and one of our local ministers. It was their final meeting, and when it was over, the Minister decided to be nice to me and, shaking my hand, said 'Thank you very much for your help, your Arabic was brilliant.' Of course I had to summon all my strength not to burst out laughing.

The only person who could see the funny side of the compliment was a young Chechen university lecturer, Alibek. We had met before briefly and I knew that he was fluent in English and could read Arabic. I noticed how he was staring down at the floor with maximum concentration. When the farewell ceremony was over, Alibek came up to me.

'It's an outstanding linguistic phenomenon, Sonia, speaking English and uttering Arabic at the same time!'

'Our educated comrade minister is an outstanding phenomenon! I thought I would die laughing!'

'I was afraid of that myself. Your profession must be full of surprises.'

'It has been recently.'

'Do you need a lift home? My brother's waiting for me in his car.'

'Oh, thank you, if it's not too much trouble.'

I could not have imagined then that soon Alibek and I would meet under different circumstances.

My first real interpreting assignment was quite unexpected. I was asked to meet the representatives of one of the Californian agricultural companies. The purpose of their visit, alfalfa seed production opportunities in Chechnya, and the fact that I was expected to interpret for the talks, too, was announced to me only on the way to the airport. Obviously for the employees of the local Ministry of Agriculture my profession was a mystery. The fact that I had graduated as a teacher and had a qualification as a translator specialising in oil refinery processes did not catch their attention. I tried to explain to them the

48

difference, but they did not have much choice with the interpreters available locally, so all I could do was accept the challenge.

The representatives of the American agricultural company arrived. The entire delegation consisted of two men. One of them, Dr. Holmes, was older and looked more like a laboratory researcher, the other one, Dr. Shaw, seemed to be more down to earth. I had to confess that, faced with such famous names from the world of literature, I had been tempted to introduce myself as Anna Karenina. They laughed. The ice was broken and after the first five minutes of conversation I decided that they were both nice men. But I could hardly say the same about the representative who had been sent from the Ministry of Agriculture in Moscow to accompany them. There was an air of superiority in his crude manners so frequent in communist times in government employees, who were nothing but ordinary clerks in their own offices, but acquired VIP status as soon as they arrived in a province on a business trip. I had a strong desire to avoid him as much as possible.

I had to explain to the Americans the situation with my agricultural terminology and suggested we work out our own system of interpretation. I said I would need some time before the talks when they could explain to me in general terms what they were going to say. The system worked quite well and by the end of the next day, still struggling with their accent, I was able to maintain professional communication between the parties. Part of the time we spent driving in the fields and visiting collective farms. I climbed with them on to the giant "Belarus" tractor when they needed to check the quality of the cut grass, interpreted their comments on the local soils, crawled beside them on my knees and got all muddy looking closely at the irrigation systems. My working day sometimes started at about seven in the morning and finished close to midnight, but professionally I never felt happier in my whole life. I became their shadow and loved every minute of it. The only inconvenience was that I was starving most of the time. Because I had to interpret the conversation during their meals as well, I did not really have time to eat, and my plate full of delicatessen usually left the table hardly touched at all. But at some point the Americans noticed this and from then on they tried to give me some time at the table free of talking.

There were lots of funny moments to add to my collection of party jokes. Once when we were driving past a pond and the local manager started explaining about the pedigree of ducks. I was thirsty and hot. My brain was on fire. 'Whatever is he talking about? Who cares about your blooming ducks, man?' But the job had to be done. I started a sentence and could not remember the English word for "drake". 'Well,' I said, 'the duck and her husband…'.

To my great relief, the Moscow Ministry representative did not take part in our field escapades. The Americans and I became so friendly that I was really sorry when their visit was over. They arranged a date for their next visit in a year's time, but a year was too long a period of time for our country. The process of political reconstruction was in full swing. And what a pity, I never met them again.

After their visit I did some more work for the Ministry of Agriculture, feeling more confident and relaxed with every new assignment.

In the meantime *perestroika* was opening up new possibilities for the people of Russia. During the Soviet period all property, as well as the means of production, had been collective. In agriculture there were only collective farms or state farms. Enterprises in industry and even in services and the hospitality business were all state-owned. There were private tutors and dressmakers, but they advertised their services by word of mouth only, and kept them hidden from nosey neighbours.

At the end of the 1980s a new trend was introduced into Russian industry. It was called a "co-operative movement". Now every farmer, baker or hairdresser could register his own "co-operative enterprise" – a private company – and enjoy his independence as long he paid his taxes.

The number of small cafés selling ice cream and fizzy drinks grew like mushrooms in the forest after rain. The next were dentists, garages, electrical and household equipment repair shops and so on. Grozny was bubbling with newly opened possibilities. The population of the city was hardly more than six hundred thousand, but the locals had always been quick-witted and highly active people. I remember reading somewhere the observation that landscape influences people's character. Among other things, it was claimed that if the river passing through a place was fast-flowing and bubbly, the local population would adopt these qualities too. The river Sunzha passing through Grozny was very fast on its way to the Terek, which flows into the Caspian Sea. Up to recent times it had always been covered with greasy spots of oil residues, another feature of the river connected to the history of the place itself.

To return to the co-operative movement and its influence in my own life, I need to mention that at some stage the owners of the co-operatives decided to organise their own union. Within a year they were strong enough to look for foreign partners to whom they could sell their produce and they were even looking into the possibility of buying equipment and other goods abroad. This was the time when I was offered a job as a secretary, translator and representative of the Union.

When my colleague and friend of many years, Larissa, was visiting me, she mentioned that there was a vacancy in one of her friend's new enterprises. She did not know the details but said that her friend was reliable. She knew him from when she had worked at the University after leaving school and could recommend him as a smart and decent man. When she named him, all I had to say was, 'Isn't it a small world, Larissa? I met Alibek once when I was interpreting for the Ministry. He gives the impression of someone with a good brain.'

'He does. He was writing a thesis for a PhD in maths when I worked as a laboratory assistant at the University. He's a gifted fellow. By the way, he was brought up by his grandfather, a mullah.'

'Really? I didn't notice anything especially religious about him. I think he's good fun. Did you by any chance know him really well? Please, Larissa, I know that expression on your face!'

'Well, we were young, both single, so…well, nothing serious, just a fling. He's married now with two children and as far as I know he's a very devoted husband.'

'This is an important piece of information, thank you, 007.'

'You're welcome. Why 007? I can't see any resemblance.'

'The method, my dear. Anyway, joking aside, what kind of company is it? Did he tell you?'

'It has something to do with the co-operatives. Just give

him a call, he will tell you all about it himself.'

At the interview Alibek told me that he was happy that we had met before and he knew me as an interpreter, but the new job was much more than that.

I eagerly accepted my new responsibilities. From the start it was exciting to learn how to use a PC. With the help of manuals and a lot of trial and error, I was able to type the file of the Union Constitution. Throughout the years of my written translation work, sitting behind dusty library shelves over piles of boring refinery magazines and volumes of laboratory tests, I had dreamt of some high-flying job with business trips to Moscow, Leningrad or other big cities. I always envied people who could break with their routine and "hit the road". Now I had that privilege myself. I made trips to the big international exhibitions in Moscow as the Union representative. How proud I was when, armed only with my business card, I used to come back with suitcases full of samples, and signed papers entitled "Protocols of Intention in Co-operation". My new job was definitely a success. Either my beginner's enthusiasm made a good impression on behalf of the Union, or it was a time of international commercial awareness of the huge new market opening up in the territory of the former Soviet Union.

After the introduction of the first private businesses into the Soviet Union, the next step in joining the world market was a new form of international co-operation, Joint Venture Companies, or JVs as they were known. These became an intermediate stage between the state-owned enterprises and the stock-holding type of companies. Goodness only knows where the name came from, but the idea itself looked attractive for both Russian and foreign parties. It was a "venture" for the latter, anyway, and many of them took their chance.

On one of my return flights from Moscow after another exhibition, I met one of my distant cousins, Andrei. So distant that we had probably met no more than once or twice before, maybe at a funeral. I remembered that someone had told me he had made a career in electronics and became deputy director of one the biggest companies in Northern Caucasus, and I knew the company produced computerised equipment for the oil industry. When we saw each other in the queue at the flight registration desk I was sure he asked me how I was just to be polite. I gave him a brief account of things. He said he had totally forgotten I was a translator. Never really troubled to remember, I thought. Andrei probably realised this did not sound very nice, and tried to make up for his clumsiness. He asked for a seat next to mine and we spent the whole flight from Moscow to Grozny talking. As the flight was more than two hours, he had enough time to tell me about his family and work, and to mention in between that he was desperate for a reliable assistant in one of his new joint ventures.

'Well, Andrei, as I've just told you, I am absolutely happy with what I'm doing at the moment. I've been with the Union for a year. I feel as if I've taken a full course in marketing with all my trips to industrial exhibitions. Now we're working on a new project, relocating businesses from Jordan to Chechnya.'

'Why do they want to be relocated?'

'Some ethnic Chechens from Jordan are eager to return to their original motherland. They migrated more than a century ago, first to Turkey, where they could survive only if they assimilated with the local population, then to Jordan. They managed to settle in Jordan and have lived in their own community up to now. Some of them have even achieved a certain social status with royalty there. Now a number of ethnic Chechens are looking for investment opportunities to ensure their life here. I can't tell you more about it, but with this project I might have a chance to go abroad.'

'Have you ever been abroad?' asked Andrei.

'You're joking! Not with my background of having a priest for a great grandfather. He was named "an enemy of the people" and sent to a labour camp. I didn't have the slimmest chance in communist times.'

'Was it your maternal great grandfather?'

'Yes, my granny Anastasia's father.'

'Yes, I see. That's why I've never heard about it.'

'Well, you know, it wasn't something to be mentioned in small talk. My grandparents were very secretive about it right up to the moment the rehabilitation papers arrived in the mid-sixties.'

'Yes, I understand very well. Did your granddad read maths in the Oil Institute? I remember an article about him in the local paper when he died. About ten years ago?'

'Sixteen, actually. He died the year I got married. As grandma said, "one man is in and another one is out."'

'Sorry if I sound badly informed again, are you still married?'

'No, I'm divorced. I have two daughters. Alexandra is thirteen and Lisa's eleven. My grandma Anastasia lives with us. All these post-Soviet changes, even church services on the television, are like an answer to her prayers. She's a tiny old lady, a bit weak physically, but still very strong in her mind and she has an amazing sense of humour.'

The flight was nearly over and our conversation dried up too. In a quarter of an hour we would be back to our everyday routine, and probably wouldn't meet again for years. But suddenly Andrei turned to me.

'Listen, Sonechka, what would you say if I were to suggest you start working for the JV next week, and accompany me to Hong Kong in five months' time? You said you wanted to go abroad. I don't expect your answer straight away. Tomorrow is Saturday. I am sure you don't work at weekends. I sometimes do. Why don't you come over to my office and we could consider all the pros and cons together. I really need you, believe me.'

'Okay, thank you, Andrei, I will come, but I can't promise anything now. What are you doing at this JV of yours? Electronic jigs?'

'No, my dear cousin, we are producing microwave ovens together with a world famous South Korean brand.'

'South Korean? Are you kidding? Russia doesn't have diplomatic relations with South Korea!'

'Aha, now you are interested! See you tomorrow at 12. We can have lunch at my place after our chat. I live within walking distance of work. Karina would be glad to see you, and it's about time you met your nieces too.'

'Will your invitation for lunch still be valid if my answer is negative?'

'Don't be silly! Of course it will!'

A couple of months later when I had already been with the JV for a while, a female colleague explained to me why I was the ideal option for Andrei at that time. It was not only because he was impressed with my experience and skills. He had been foolish enough to start an affair with the young university graduate who worked as a PA and translator for him. A week before I met him at the airport, someone had told his wife about it and she had given him an ultimatum to fire his lover, or otherwise she would divorce him. So that explained the extraordinarily warm welcome I had received at Andrei's house.

However it was not due to a sudden burst of family feelings that I decided to accept Andrei's offer. He had actually been very matter-of-fact in our conversation the day after our meeting in Moscow Vnukovo airport. First of all, he explained to me the structure of the JV. It was a four-part partnership. The two state enterprises on the Russian side were both big producers with powerful resources, including space and trained manpower. One of them was a local firm where Andrei was the deputy director, the other was a similar company situated in Central Russia. The foreign part of the partnership consisted of one of the well-known South Korean electronic home appliance producers and a small Indian company, specialising in dealerships with electronics firms. Because there were no diplomatic relations between the Soviet Union and South Korea, a direct commercial partnership was impossible and for this reason they used the Indian company as a legal representative in their partnership instead.

'Now that you understand the structure of the JV, Sonia, I'd like you to see our production lines.'

We left the office through the back door and, crossing the car park, walked over to Andrei's Lada.

'Sorry, it's not a Merc,' Andei smiled, 'but it's better to be safe than sorry. I prefer to be modest and not attract attention. I assure you, dear cousin, if you dream of driving a posh car, with this job you'll get there. We've not discussed your salary yet, but it would be at least twenty per cent higher than your present one, with monthly and quarterly benefits. Well, here we are.'

It had taken us less than twenty minutes to drive to the other premises of the plant. Andrei drove in showing his ID pass to the security man. The building inside was surprisingly clean and light. A dozen men in blue uniforms were assembling microwave ovens on the conveyor line.

'The Koreans send us partially assembled ovens declared as spare-parts. All we do is just add a couple of parts, test the ovens and pack them in boxes. Everything is produced by the South Korean company, even the boxes. You can see it by the brand name.'

'It doesn't look like a very sophisticated process. Can I ask you something, Andrei? Wouldn't it be easier for the South Koreans to sell their product direct? Oh, silly me! They can't, because of customs charges. They would be much higher for a finished product. Am I right? And it's also because there are no diplomatic relations with South Korea.'

'I wasn't mistaken when I thought you were a smart girl.'

'But do you realise, Andrei, the country is changing very quickly. In a year or two they could be all over the place themselves, your Korean partners.'

'Oh, yes, I do realise this. But it would be a different country then with a different type of economy. And just now we're swimming in this particular stream and we're making the most of it, believe me.'

He took the keys from the security desk and we went down a long corridor to the other part of the premises where there were two more conveyor lines ready for operation.

'Look, Sofia, these two lines are intended for the other goods we are going to assemble. The next one will be for washing machines. We haven't made up our minds about the third one yet, we need to do some more market research. What I'm trying to show you here is that this

JV has a future. You know how our people are hungry for good domestic equipment. What kind of choice did we have before with only "Minsk" fridges and "Volga" washing machines?'

'Yes, and even they were rationed. I could do with a washing machine myself, by the way.'

'Do you have a microwave?'

'A microwave? Not on my salary!'

'Okay, now let's get to the point and discuss your salary.'

'Not yet, Andrei, I would prefer to have a job description first.'

'The printed part of it is in my car, you can read it on the way back. As for the other part, let's call it our gentleman's agreement. I mentioned before that I need a reliable assistant. Confidentiality will be the most important part of our deal. I must admit I can't promise you a strictly eight-hour working day and weekends off, but I can promise that your overtime will be well paid. As soon as we are back I'll show you your exact rates of pay. I tell you what, shall we go straight for lunch and I'll ring the office and ask my accountant to send me the papers with the courier?'

'Is your accountant working today, too?'

'Yes, she is. A lovely lady, by the way. I have known her since my student days.'

'Well, Andrei, thank you very much for the tour. But I shall need to give at least a week's notice. I can't just go and leave the place.'

Andrei's offer was so generous I knew I simply could not afford to ignore it. So I started the next Monday part-time, going back to the Union every afternoon to sort out things over there. My former employer, Alibek, was not at all happy that I was leaving, but he understood the situation. It was enough to mention that Andrei, was "family", which was very important to every Chechen or any other Caucasian-born person. They expected everyone to be as devoted to their roots as they were themselves. And there was another thing. When we were having a cup of tea together before I actually left, Alibek, normally quick with a good joke, became extraordinarily serious.

'Sofia, I have to tell you something very important. No matter how happy you are with your job now, you have to think of leaving Grozny very soon. Terrible things are going to happen in Chechnya. It will be dangerous for Russians to stay here, believe me. A massive confrontation is coming up, Sonia.'

'What do you mean, a confrontation? Between whom? Between Russians and Chechens?'

'No. It will be between the Chechens themselves, but Russians will be the first ones to suffer.'

'Thank you Alibek, but I really don't have anywhere to go. All my life is here. I don't have any close relatives in Russia. I can't even think of leaving.'

'Please, Sofia, remember what I've just told you.'

She was full of plans and very optimistic about her future. Who could blame her? The whole country was euphoric about the changes. *Perestroika*! Remake! Mikhail Gorbachev was like an old tailor, confident in his skills. He knew the coat was old, but it used to be so comfortable and familiar, and he thought it could still be worn for some time if it were cleaned properly and then turned inside out, given new sleeves and a few patches on the back. But the coat was dirty, shabby and beyond repair. It fell to pieces the moment it was touched.

When The Soviet Union did fall apart, at first it was quiet

and peaceful in Chechnya. In public speeches the local leaders liked to mention the common sense and loyalty of Chechens and Ingush in a period when political chaos threatened to ruin stability in the country. Unfortunately, the peace did not last long. Soon the confrontation started. It was a fight between the supporters of the former local government and the new political party of the separatists. The confrontation literally took the form of two separate crowds each occupying one of the two main squares in the centre of the city. Lenin Square was in front of the old Communist Party headquarters building. Revolution Square was framed by the Ministry on one side and the new Communist Party headquarters on the other. The debates between the two crowds were going on day and night. There was no so-called "Russian-speaking population" among the crowds. This was a new term which appeared in the official vocabulary after the demolition of the Soviet Union. The term defined not only Russians, but also people of other nationalities, who did not speak the language of the original population but used Russian, the official language for communication everywhere in the former Soviet Union. The debates were held mainly in the Chechen language.

Everyone was waiting for a reaction from Moscow, but the Kremlin remained silent. The whole population, including the common Chechens not involved in politics, wondered why. One of the possible explanations was as follows: the recently converted communists were too busy keeping up the appearance of being a new democratic government in the eyes of the international community to send troops to take control, if not by force, then by a demonstration of it. That was what they would normally have done in Soviet times. They would demonstrate their power, their ability to control the situation. People used to say that there were always troops somewhere near Rostov-on-Don, within two hundred kilometres, ready to be posted to Chechnya.

Many things happened after I made my decision to leave Grozny. Time proved that it was the only possible decision. My joint venture company where I enjoyed working so much, was closed under circumstances usually defined in contracts as "force-majeure". Andrei tried his best to keep the head company going. He said he could find a job there for me, too, but I knew it would be general secretarial duties. I wanted to continue my international career. So I took a new job in a company providing overseas businessmen with all necessary services for commercial talks. There was a good reason for choosing that work. The company had a contingency plan to move from Grozny to Orel, a town in Central Russia, should the situation turn out to be life-threatening. But even then I kept hoping it would somehow miraculously sort itself out.

My new job was all right. Before *perestroika*, Grozny and the whole of Chechnya had been a region closed to foreigners for strategic reasons, mainly because of the oil refineries. Now it was frequently visited by the bravest or most suspect of overseas businessmen. My responsibilities with the new company were not very complicated: taking charge of the conference room, interpreting during the negotiations and so on. My first assignment was a construction project. A Turkish entrepreneur was going to build a dental factory to produce acrylic teeth. The Chechen side was represented by the Chief Dentist of the Republic. The terms of payment for construction services and equipment installation were to be bartered. The word "barter" had sneaked into the commercial vocabulary of the former Soviet Union and had become the most popular means of payment. It could have been substituted by the words "natural exchange", the way trade started before money was invented. But "barter" was a foreign word and former Soviet directors who had studied capitalist economy from a Marxist viewpoint in their Institutes, liked to use English words. It seemed to give them a feeling of a new self-respect and importance. They also liked the word "manager" and especially "general manager". In the case of the dental factory certain oil refinery products were to be supplied as barter to pay for the factory.

The Chief Dentist was a stout man with nice social manners and a clear, straightforward way of expressing his ideas. I didn't have any difficulty interpreting for him. The difficulties with the Turk were not of a linguistic nature. From the very beginning of the talks I noticed that, as soon as I turned my back to set up a flip chart, his eyes were all over me. He was definitely a "pinching-the-bottoms-of-hotel-maids" type. As I was little more than a maid from his point of view, he tried a number of tricks, ranging from an invitation to dinner to caressing the calf of my leg with his toes under the table during a business lunch. Unfortunately for him, I was wearing rather sharp heeled shoes that afternoon. After that he kept his feet and propositions to himself. From a business point of view the current stage of the talks finished with a positive result not only for the "tooth entrepreneur", but for me as well. My boss was pleased with my work. I was paid with "greens" for the first time in my life.

I decided to give a little party at home for my friends to relieve the oppressive atmosphere of fear and uncertainty. I thought a party would be something to cheer everyone up. It would be like making a statement: life goes on, ladies and gentlemen! It was Thursday, and before leaving the office, I made a list of my guests, all my close friends. Two couples and four single ladies! The girls were not doing well recently. Like me, Larissa and Vera were divorced, Mila my schoolmate and Lena, whom I had met through Mila, were both single but not lesbians, as they pointed out when introducing themselves. The two couples were my men friends, Stas and Nikolai, with their wives, Masha and Nina respectively, whom I eventually befriended, too. As far as I knew, Larissa had started seeing a new man recently and I hoped she would bring him. I needed three more men to give the party a good balance. Well, at least two. With so many people having left Grozny it was a problem. Never mind, I would browse through my very personal telephone book.

So it would be a meal for twelve anyway. Then I realised that nobody was going out after dark nowadays, it was too dangerous. All right, let it be a daytime party. Sunday lunch, as they call it in Britain. I looked at my watch and thought it would be nice to do some shopping tonight. Perhaps I could pick up some things at the city market and do the rest the next day. With the Russian economic blockade of Chechnya after it had declared its independence there was not much choice of food. But we Soviet housewives were well trained to make a meal out of nothing. I'd better do it the other way round, buy the ingredients first and then make a menu. So I went to the market to check on supplies and get whatever nice things I could find. First of all I approached the stalls selling homemade cottage cheese. There were pots of soft freshly made cottage cheese and cakes of solid more mature cheese, kept in brine, jars of sour cream and

64

milk, bars of golden butter. The quantity and choice were incomparably smaller. Farmers now were afraid of taking trips to the market. Nevertheless, I found a good portion of cottage cheese for my hot starter, *khachapuri*, a kind of Georgian savoury pasty. Now that it was difficult to buy bread, I was proud that I had bought a whole 75-kilo sack of white flour and a smaller 30-kilo sack of sugar before the embargo started. I thought if Yeltsin by any chance realised how stupid it had been to lay the blame for his own wrong policy on the innocent subjects of his own country, and decided to lift the economic blockade, I could still make use of my flour and sugar. It was important that the presence of those two sacks in the cellar made our granny happy. Otherwise, having experienced famine both during the First World War and Revolution, and then during the Second World War, she would worry herself to death. As soon as the Chechens proclaimed their independence she never stopped worrying that we would die of starvation.

I also needed some vegetables for salads, and I thought it would be nice if I could find some caviar. You could always buy fresh caviar in the city market in Grozny. The Caspian Sea, the main source of Russian caviar, was only three hours' drive from Grozny. My granny served it for breakfast, on a buttered slice of bread, with a mug of freshly made sweet white coffee. I did not realise at that time that the kilo jar of caviar in our fridge would be a luxury in Moscow. In Grozny it was cheaper than the same quantity of sausages. The fishermen's wives regularly knocked on the door offering to sell it.

Meeting Mark

I had been speculating on the better way of serving caviar as a cold starter: I could spread spoonfuls of caviar on halved hard-boiled eggs or bake tiny tarts and fill them. On my way to the fish stalls I noticed a man wearing a woollen check scarf tied under the collar of his jacket, walking between the rows of market stalls. If he wanted to advertise himself as a foreigner he couldn't do better. This way of wearing his scarf spared him from sticking a sign on his forehead. Curious, I watched him coming up to the jars of caviar and asking '*Skolko?*' 'How much?' The vendor started by shouting his price, then showing it on his fingers, then at last writing it on a piece of paper. I interrupted this vigorous exchange and asked if I could try the merchandise. I did what people usually do at my city market: held out my fisted hand. The stall assistant placed a little bit of caviar on the upper surface of my fist. I licked the caviar off and asked if he had some other kind of brine. I realised that the foreigner was watching the whole operation with an expression of horror mixed with respect.

'Is it good?' he asked, '*khorosho?*'

'It's not bad, but I prefer the freshly brined one,' I answered him in English.

After caviar had been chosen and bought by us both with my help, the stranger introduced himself.

'I'm Mark Stuart, by the way. Thank you ever so much for your help. Your English is brilliant. Did you study it in the UK?'

'Thanks. No, I didn't. I studied it at the local University. I'm Sofia. If you need some more help with your shopping, be my guest. I'm going to buy some vegetables now and then probably some chicken or meat.'

'Well, thank you, I'll have a look if you don't mind.'

That was how I met him.

Mark had really dropped into the market just to pass the time. He was fed up and felt foolish. The whole thing about this trip was silly and childish. It was his second day in the town and he was thinking of changing his flight and leaving the place tomorrow. He did not have any intention of buying anything and had approached the stalls with something looking like caviar out of pure curiosity. And then that girl had appeared. She was pretty, and she spoke English fluently, with a trace of an accent that sounded more continental than Russian. After six months in Karaganda in Kazakhstan, and frequent trips to Moscow, he was used to the fact that most Russian girls were pretty, especially the young ones. High cheek bones, radiant skin, nice bums. A very good-looking race. And, as he knew by now, passionate in bed too.

'So what are you doing in Grozny apart from shopping in the city market? Is it business or pleasure?' asked Sofia as they walked through the market.

'Wasting my time,' Mark wanted to answer, but then thought of the impression he would make and changed his mind. He already knew that he wanted to make a good impression.

'Well, yes, it's business. I've been asked to do some market research for my company.'

'What kind of business are you in?' asked Sofia.

'I'm in a sort of holiday club business, time-share. Have you heard about it, Miss…'.

'Sofia, please call me Sofia. I know from my experience as an interpreter that Russian surnames are tongue twisters

67

for foreigners. What kind of research is it? Do you mean your company is going to build a holiday resort over here? Oh, sorry, Mark, there's something I'd like to have a look at over there.'

They were moving now between the stalls of green-groceries, and the girl, Sofia, abandoned him for a while to choose her vegetables. Mark was watching her and the more he watched the more he liked what he saw. Her quick smile, flashing her perfect even teeth, the way she pushed the fringe of short brown hair from her forehead, even the way she was dressed, in that stylish but modest business lady's way you wouldn't expect to find in a Russian province. It would be nice to know her better. Sofia came back to him.

'Have you found anything you like, Mark?'

'I have', he thought, but he said 'No, I've changed my mind about buying anything tonight. Can I ask you to join me for a coffee somewhere nearby, so I can tell you more about my business here and perhaps you would be kind enough to give me some advice? Let me help you with your bags.'

'Thank you. There's a nice café not far from here, but it's overlooking the old Lenin square, with that everlasting meeting. It could be closed. But actually it's getting late. I think I'd better take a taxi home. Sorry, Mark, we locals prefer to stay indoors after dark nowadays. I wouldn't go far from your hotel if I were you. This is my business card with my office and home telephone numbers. If you need any professional advice please call me later tonight or tomorrow and we can arrange a meeting.'

End of the passage from Sofia's book

Mark would not have let her go if he had had the choice. He saw her out to the street, helped her into a taxi, and when she waved her hand, moving away, was surprised to feel a strange emptiness somewhere in his stomach, as if he had known her all his life and now she was leaving him forever. The feeling only lasted for a fraction of second.

'Is she something special or am I just bored? I definitely wouldn't mind getting into her knickers'.

That was the most likely explanation he could think of. He would give it an hour and call her. Suddenly he realised that the piece of paper with her name and telephone numbers was all he had.

'What if she didn't take me seriously and the numbers are false? For goodness sake, what's up with me? Why am I so worried? I don't even know her.'

But he was already rushing back to his hotel to dial the numbers.

Mark Stuart

The real reason why Mark Stuart, a forty-year-old British salesman from a Spanish resort, found himself on a rainy day in early spring in the small local airport of the place that proudly called itself Grozny, capital of the Chechen-Ingush Republic, was not quite clear even to himself.

Grozny and Chechnya were words from his childhood memories. Once a year his widowed paternal grandfather used to take Mark and his older brother Peter from Paisley in Scotland, where they all lived, to Morecambe, the English seaside resort. The beauty of this trip for the boys was in its unconditional freedom. This included stuffing themselves with ice cream and candyfloss, skipping proper meals and bed times. Daily baths when nasty soap stung your eyes were not compulsory either. These were things they couldn't dream of at home where their English mother tried hard to bring them up in style and order, ruling her little empire with strict discipline, often in the absence of their Scottish father, who, they knew, was working hard to support them all and had just started to climb the career ladder in a big national company. The trips to Morecambe were also fascinating for them because of two other things: a donkey by the name of Sausage, a big friend of Mark and Peter, and uncle Steven, an old friend of granddad. Sausage liked white bread, saved for him from the hotel breakfasts, and biscuits obtained from other sources. He would take the treat very carefully from your palm, looking at you with his big sad eyes, and let you stroke his velvet coat. But the best bit was riding him along the beach imagining that you were a cowboy somewhere in the Prairies. Yahoo!

Uncle Steven and granddad would spend hours sitting on the terrace of a restaurant on the front overlooking the sea, and talking about the old days over a pint or two. And while the boys were riding their ponies, imagining their heroic future, the old men in their memories travelled back to their past. Their Prairies were a place somewhere far away called Chechnya. They were both retired oil field engineers, who had spent some time investigating resources in different parts of the world, including the southern brink of the Russian Empire, where they had happened to be in the first decade of the twentieth century.

Most of the time Mark and Peter were too busy with their own pursuits and paid little attention to the old men's conversation, but some details nevertheless remained in Mark's memory.

Granddad died of asthma in his late eighties when Mark was still at school. Being one of his next of kin, he had been asked to help in clearing his house. It was sad and sometimes boring for a teenager to go through the things once treasured by the deceased. Books and old papers cluttered the place. It was then that he found a dusty cardboard box, tied with an elastic band, behind the old books in granddad's mahogany bookcase.

Mark opened the box. It contained shares of the Grozny Anglo-Russian Oil Company and some old letters and photographs. It was like returning to Morecambe and his childhood memories. He opened one of the yellowish envelopes and read the formal notification of closure from the company board. The other letters were written in French in an elegant ladylike handwriting. In some of the photographs Mark recognised granddad and uncle Steven. One of those photographs was rather intriguing.

It bore the logo of a photo studio in Russian. In the picture his grandfather and uncle Steven were looking at him, both very young and dressed in Cossack uniforms, smiling and bending their heads, looking down at some unknown young lady, sitting in a chair between them. She was pretty in a somewhat unusual way: her cheekbones were high, her face was outlined in a perfect oval. But most interesting was the expression of that face – her lips were not smiling, but she looked as if she could suddenly burst into a smile or even laughter. The smile was already there, in her lovely eyes, in the mockingly raised line of her thin black eyebrows. She was dressed in something looking like a Marie-Antoinette period gown and had a powdered wig. This dress and a feathered mask in her hand suggested that the picture had been taken when the young men were on their way to a fancy dress ball.

There was partly faded writing on the other side of the picture, but it too was in French, like the letters. The handwriting looked pretty much the same. The only words Mark could recognise were the names: William, which was his granddad's name, Steven and Nadya. The latter was obviously the name of the girl. Was she Russian? If so, why was she writing in French? And was she someone special for granddad or maybe for uncle Steven? Mark thought, that he would never know the answer to that question now that granddad was no longer here, and uncle Steven had gone even before him, two years earlier. As nobody wanted the box, he kept it himself.

Many things had happened to Mark since then: college in Paisley, first job in catering. He had travelled a lot, taking jobs overseas, one after another. Once he made an attempt to settle down in his own country. He married Lucy, a girl he met on one of his Christmas visits to Britain. Did he love her? He didn't really know. He definitely loved her gorgeous breasts, unexpectedly large for her slim, tiny figure. They ended up practically every day of his Christmas holiday in bed in his hotel room, and by the end of the holiday he asked her if she wanted to come and visit him in the Caribbean where he was working as a restaurant manager. She followed him soon afterwards and he was glad when she decided to stay. Three months later she said she was pregnant and they announced their engagement. They decided it would be better to start their family in Britain, a decision that made both his and her parents happy. They took a licence for a pub in the crowded city centre of Leeds where her family lived. When the preparations for the wedding were in full swing, it turned out that she was not pregnant after all and that discovery left him with a sour taste of having been manipulated. But she conceived soon after the wedding and gave birth to a beautiful girl who became the main person in his life. Mark was too busy with the pub and if he had any free time he would spend it playing with Ann, his little daughter. He shared a bed with Lucy and they made love from time to time, but the passion had gone and they hardly talked to each other. He couldn't blame Lucy when she left him, and he didn't really miss her as long as he could still spend time with little Ann. In fact, he was pleased to be a bachelor again, he felt his high sexual drive was back, there were plenty more fish in the sea. He started an affair with Susan, his barmaid. Lucy sued him for divorce on the grounds of infidelity and disappeared soon afterwards, taking Ann with her. After many fruitless attempts to find them, Mark was miserable at first, but then in the course of time felt better, especially after taking a new job as a time-share representative in one of the

Scottish resorts where his parents owned a week of time-share. Following his new career, he soon went abroad to Portugal, where he spent a number of years. After that he moved to Spain.

He lived the life of every British bachelor in Southern Europe: recovering from hangovers in the morning by jumping into a cold swimming pool, getting dressed in a freshly pressed polo-shirt and light trousers (no shirts and ties, but no jeans or shorts either). Later, after the first cup of strong Spanish coffee in the local café, he was ready to start his working day with the morning staff meeting, intended to build up enthusiasm in the sales reps. The culmination of the day was a personal presentation which would either end up with a sale or with nothing. If a deal had been signed you were overwhelmed with a feeling of victory, pleased with yourself whilst everyone else was pleased with you, and you couldn't wait till the end of your working day to celebrate with a drink or two, or more, knowing that you deserved it. If the sale was unsuccessful, all your built-up energy, your desire and expectations came to nothing and you couldn't help but feel betrayed and frustrated. Goodness, you had tried so hard, the deal was nearly there and they didn't want to go ahead! 'Never mind, next time,' you would say to yourself, but it didn't work and off you went straight to the bar to unwind.

The rest of the night would sometimes be shared with a woman, a single holidaymaker pursuing the same goal: to unwind. Some of them would stay till the end of the week, they would even make plans to meet again, giving each other promises no one seriously meant to keep. A great life without obligations and responsibilities. Isn't that every hedonist's idea of paradise? Those were his afternoon thoughts.

But there were also the early morning thoughts. With the first rays of hot Mediterranean sun, they would come and wake him and force him out of bed and on to the deserted sea front, bringing memories of his childhood, and mixing them with images of his time with Ann, his little girl. He would stare at a breathtaking view of the rising sun, overwhelmed by memories of her voice and touch, the smell of her skin and the wet curls of her hair in the mornings, and tears would blur the perfect picture of paradise before him. That was the moment of truth when he didn't need to pretend that he enjoyed his flamboyant, playboy life. It was purposeless and empty, but who cared? Nobody did actually.

When it was rumoured that the developer of a famous seaside resort had come up with the idea of expanding the market into the former Soviet Union territories, Mark had been the first one in the recruitment agency. The high season was over, it was quiet and boring at the resort and in the town, and Mark was happy to be occupied with packing and planning. He was appointed to supervise the opening of a new time-share presentation "deck" in Karaganda, a small mining town in Kazakhstan. It was a strange trip. He stayed in Moscow for a couple of days, before flying to Alma-Aty, and then to Karaganda.

After the grand Art-Deco Metropole hotel not far from the Kremlin in Moscow and the Central hotel in Alma-Ata, decorated with oriental luxury, Karaganda with its run down buildings and the absence of hot water in the taps of his shabby hotel bathroom gave him the feeling that the whole enterprise was going to be a total disaster. The next morning, when there was still no hot water, he tried to find a way of communicating with the hotel receptionist, but her English was as bad as his Russian, and to explain the problem Mark had to drag the woman into his suite and into the bathroom, and make his statement by pointing to the tap and shouting "*Nyet* water!" He was very surprised when the receptionist in her turn, catching him by his sleeve, showed him a tap on the radiator, with an empty glass jar underneath. After further shouting and energetic gesticulation, Mark understood that he could use radiator water for shaving. As for the hygiene of the rest of his body, this was still unclear.

Things started to look up when, an hour later, there was a knock on the door and a middle-aged lady came in introducing herself as Galina, his assistant and interpreter. She took over all the complicated negotiations with the hotel staff. With the next knock on the door an athletic looking young man entered the room and was introduced by Galina as his chauffeur and bodyguard, Sergei, a former KGB agent. It sounded like a surreal James Bond film. Mark couldn't help but laugh, and, forgetting his frustration, decided to relax and go with the flow.

After such an intriguing start to the day, his work gradually slid into a normal routine. Galina and Sergei from now on accompanied him everywhere. First of all they took him to the office and presentation facilities. He was happy with the premises, which were well equipped with the latest technology. He also met the team of future sales representatives. They were shy and timid at first, but eager to learn. Mark arranged a training schedule immediately.

In a couple of days, with the help of Galina and Sergei, he moved from his awful hotel into a rented apartment. They recommended that he buy a pair of fur winter boots and a *shapka* fur hat, advice he was reluctant to take at first, but when the temperature dropped down to minus 10°C, he was happy to buy both, again with their help, at the local market. The boots were made in Finland, and the mink *shapka* was made locally.

His life now was totally different. His colleagues, local people, were friendly and open with him. Their way of life was amazingly different from life in Europe, more like the post-war time of rationing with its shortages, black market and vegetables from the allotments. His hosts, the office clerks, computer specialist and accountants, invited him into their homes, treated him to a tour of their cellars, where they proudly showed Mark the boxes of potatoes, carrots and other root vegetables mixed with sand for preservation, the batteries of jars with homemade pickled vegetables and jams, explaining that they had grown and produced all this themselves. It would help them to feed their families through the long winter. At times like this he appreciated the way he used to live, not even noticing the convenience of supermarket food.

In Karaganda everything was unbelievably cheap for him. Sometimes he liked to go shopping in the market just across the street from his apartment, where he could buy a joint of beef or pork for a dollar or two, to exercise his cooking skills. But the same prices were unaffordable for many of the local people. He was shocked when he was told that the lady employed by the company to clean his rented apartment was a qualified doctor. She worked at the local surgery, but her salary was much less than the hundred dollars a month she received as a cleaner. Looking around, Mark couldn't really understand how his employers thought they could sell ten thousand pound contracts over here. When he shared his concerns with Galina and Sergei, they just laughed, and told him not to worry.

In two weeks' time, as soon as they started their presentations, Mark realised what they meant: their audience came mostly in chauffeured cars not only from Karaganda, but from other nearby places as well. Curious, he watched the arriving crowd from his office through a convenient one-way window. There were two main groups of people, dressed according to the local fashion: the older men were mainly in black suits and ties with white shirts, so you couldn't help but think of a funeral. They were accompanied by their overweight wives, clad in silk and velvet with loads of gold jewellery. The younger men were mostly overweight too, dressed in dark red jackets or just in designer track suits and trainers. Both types of young men displayed heavy gold chains on their open necks and wrists. In contrast, their ladies were tall and slim and looked like catwalk models in their designer outfits, if it were not for the bored expressions on their heavily made-up pretty faces. Galina called the younger ones New Russians, those who had made their fortunes in the period of changing power in Russia and the former Soviet republics. She also said that it was rather dangerous to ask how they had made their money.

So the business started very successfully. Mark had a feeling of being the conductor of an orchestrated performance of some new unknown interactive type, involving the participation of the audience. Twenty tables were set out in the presentation hall which had the appearance of a good restaurant. There was a small stage, from which Mark addressed the public, telling them about the tremendous opportunities for time-share owners and showing them a promotional film where sun-tanned happy people enjoyed their lives in landscapes of Paradise. Galina was interpreting. The Russian representatives then joined each table to explain how the system worked, and Mark followed them with Galina as his shadow, taking over the pitch, answering questions and closing deals. And then came the finale with the hand shaking and victorious popping of champagne corks: "*Alle Menschen werden Brüder!*" Well, nearly.

They were happy and grateful to Mark for coming to their cold and untidy country, bringing with him the opportunity to join the happily organised capitalist world! He became their friend, their brother. Hadn't he already heard something similar? Something about the colourful beads of the newcomers? Those people already knew that everything in the world has its price and they were ready to pay. Now came the most amazing part of the performance for Mark: all the payments were made directly in cash in the back stage office. It looked as if the pages of a James Bond script had been mixed with those of The Godfather. The piles of hundred dollar bank notes were counted and checked behind the office door, guarded by two groups of dangerous-looking men, each one watching the other with the attention of boxers in the ring.

Later, Mark had been asked to take that cash out of the country on a regular basis. This casual way of handling money mesmerised him to the point of losing all sense of danger. He had been told not to worry about the Customs. They were given their share before he entered the airport. It had probably been true, because he had never been stopped or searched on any of the occasions when he was acting as a money courier.

The business in Karaganda was an outrageous success and Mark became a local celebrity. Every customer considered it an honour to have him as a guest for dinner or lunch. Galina could no longer cope single-handedly with his busy social life, and an interpreter, Katya, a very young and very pretty girl, was soon introduced to him. She was probably no more than twenty, nearly the same age as his little Ann, and he didn't dare to even think of seducing her. But, just as in a Hollywood movie, late one Sunday night she asked if she could make a long-distance call from his apartment, a favour he would do for any of his staff. He let her in and went out to the kitchen to put the kettle on, and when he came back she called him from his bedroom. Well, she was beautiful and willing and who would refuse when it was on a plate? Now he had it all, suitcases full of money, dangerous trips, a young lover who kept whispering in his ear in the night, 'I love you Marrrk, do you love me? Will you get me out of here? I want to go back to Spain with you. Will you take me to Spain, Mark?' And he kept whispering back, 'Yes, oh yes. Yes, Katya'. Wouldn't anyone?

That was how Mark spent one of the coldest and strangest winters of his life. Early in March the developer phoned him and advised him to call it a day. He was already longing to return to Europe himself. His early morning moments of truth were chasing him again. He started thinking of his daughter. What if somewhere some middle-aged bastard… . But he did not allow his imagination to go that far.

There was also a feeling of something he had forgotten to do. Once during a routine presentation, as they approached one of the tables to talk to the people and hopefully close a deal, Galina, who was translating for him that night, mentioned that this couple were Chechen. Mark started asking them about Grozny and Vladikavkaz, the names of towns that had somehow stuck in his memory. He was surprised when they told him that there was a flight once

80

a week from Alma-Aty to Grozny, and at least one flight a day from Moscow. Mark decided that he had to pay a visit, just as a gesture of respect to granddad's memory. It would be good, too, if he could make some enquiries about the old oil company papers. He would ask Martin, the developer: maybe he could do some market research for him as well. And then, who knows, he might be asked to organise an office in Grozny. The Chechens he talked to did mention that their compatriots were doing well nowadays. 'So let's make it a business trip,' decided Mark. It would give the whole adventure a sense of meaning.

That is how and why Mark arrived in Grozny, and ended up in a hotel room, nervously pacing up and down and looking at his watch, wondering when would be an appropriate time to ring the Russian lady by the name of Sofia, the lady he had met less than two hours ago, but who for some reason had not left his thoughts since. Not at all pleased with himself, Mark dialled the number.

'Ahlo?' said a child's voice at the other end.

Mark suddenly felt foolish and even more annoyed with himself. Why hadn't he asked her if she was married? But how could he?

'Hello, can I speak to Sofia, please? My name is Mark Stuart.' There was a pause, then the same voice answered in English, 'Sure. Just a moment please.'

'Hello?' Sofia's voice.

'Oh, hello. I hope you don't mind me calling you so soon. I'm afraid I really need your help, Sofia. Do you want me to call later? Are you are busy now?'

'It's all right, Mark. I know how you feel. I can imagine how difficult it must be in a place where nobody understands you. It's Friday tomorrow. Would you like to come over to my office at about one o'clock? I have an hour for lunch and you could join me if you like. Our company canteen food is not too bad, by the way.'

'Brilliant! Thank you ever so much, Sofia. And what is your company's address?'

'The address is on my business card. But Mark, I can arrange for an office car to pick you up and get you back to the hotel afterwards.'

'That would be great, thank you.'

'Now, Mark, our meeting tomorrow would be more constructive if you were to give me some idea of the kind of help you actually need.'

Mark did not want their acquaintance to slide straight down to the level of business, but she did not give him any choice. 'Well', thought Mark, 'there is nothing I can do about it. At least I'm going to see her tomorrow'. So he started telling her about his present occupation in Karaganda and the great success of their business there, and his idea of finding partners to discuss the possibility of doing the same kind of business in Grozny. Sofia listened to him very attentively, asking questions from time to time, then told him that the company she was working for could deal with the technical side of the job, like organising the place, translation and secretarial support as well as legal advice. As for local business partners, she would have to make some calls and enquiries first. That was the end of their conversation. Mark told himself that he was an idiot to dream of anything more than a brief business talk. She had probably only agreed to see him because she thought of him as a potential client. But he was mistaken.

Sofia had noticed the impression she had made on him, and for the first time in her two-year period of sexual abstinence, she felt a pleasant sensation. She enjoyed his nervousness and his haste to make the call, and she knew he was dying to make their conversation more personal. Situations like this, when a man gave all the signals of readiness for a closer relationship, had happened to her quite often before, but she had always brushed them aside quickly and firmly. Why did she feel so different about it now? 'Considering that he's here only for a short visit, isn't it rather foolish on my part?' thought Sofia. But nevertheless she was happy to think of seeing him again, and then, who could say what might happen, especially if he stayed in Grozny. Her older daughter Alexandra noticed straightaway her dreamy smile and a sort of reluctant slowness in her movements when they laid the table for supper together.

'Who was that foreigner on the phone, mum? Someone from work?'

'No, I picked him up at the market tonight, Sasha.'

'Do they sell them there? Doesn't sound like a seasonal vegetable to me, mum. Not now with all these demonstrations for the independence thing.'

'No, you're right. Anyway you may see him on Sunday. I will probably invite him to our party. What do you think?'

'Well, I don't know. Is he married?'

'I have absolutely no idea!'

'Oh, lovely! Okay, get him over here, I'll interrogate him myself.'

'Why? You can't marry him, he is too old for you.'

'Who's getting married?' granny Anastasiya joined them in the kitchen.

'Oh, hello, nana, we haven't decided yet. Maybe you?' Alexandra pulled up a chair for her. Leaning on her walking stick, with Yashka, a miniature parrot, on her shoulder, granny with her fragile bone structure and small head covered with a scarf tied at the back, looked like a bird herself. The parrot was watching the table closely from grandmother's shoulder, ready to fly down on to the board with the sliced bread. But granny, feeling his stirring movements even through her quilted jacket, caught him in time.

'Come on, you bold eagle. Very sorry, sir, you are not invited. Go and peck your seeds.'

As she carried him carefully in her dry fingers and placed him in his cage, the bird tried to express his protest in an angry stage whisper, 'Yashsha! Chcharman!' He and granny were very good friends and were the only French speakers in the family. As for the English language, Sofia had started teaching Alexandra to speak English when she was three and had then taken her to the so-called English school, where she had six hours of English per week. She was fluent in it, but had recently declared that she preferred to communicate with her mother in her native language. Lisa had taken the same route with English but, unlike Alexandra, she enjoyed making a show of speaking English in public with either her mother or her sister.

During the meal they discussed the possibility of inviting Mark for their Sunday lunch. Granny thought it was a good idea. And Sofia agreed that Mark's presence would keep them from going on and on about who had left Grozny, and when and where to, and the urgency of the same problem for the rest of them.

Friday

The next morning Sofia told her employer, the former
trade union leader, about the possible new client, without
mentioning how she had met him, and they both decided to
help him in his search for a partnership for his enterprise.
This meant that, once she had introduced him to her boss,
Sofia would be able to spend not only her lunch break,
but also some of her office time with Mark. So when the
office car brought Mark to their door at five minutes to
one, Sofia knew she was going to have a pleasant couple
of hours in the company of a handsome, well mannered
man who had fallen for her. And that awareness brought a
sparkle into her eyes and colour to her cheeks.

Their business meeting now looked more like a date,
with a moment of awkwardness at the beginning, overcome
by an inexplicable feeling of happiness in each other's
presence. Sofia introduced Mark to her boss and he joined
their discussion, so they had to change their plan to have
lunch first. The discussion did not take long, and when
Mark suggested they go for lunch, Sofia agreed. There
was a small *cheburechnaya* café across the road, where
they took a table by the window overlooking a quiet street
bordered with maple trees. Mark automatically remarked
that it must look lovely in summer time. They ordered
salads and *chebureki*, Georgian flat meat pasties, another
new food for Mark. Their conversation focused on food
and eating habits in different countries. When they had
finished their lunch, Sofia suggested they might take

advantage of the lovely sunny weather and go for a walk in the nearby park before going back to the office.

'I'm so happy that I met you, Sofia, I don't want to pretend any more that I came to discuss business. I'm here because of you. I don't know anything about you. Are you married? Who was the girl on the phone? Your daughter?'

'No, I'm divorced. And yes, that was my daughter Alexandra. She'll be fourteen next month. She's the elder of my two daughters. She is a very confident young lady, likes to be in control. Lisa, my younger daughter, calls her "the director". What about you, Mark? Are you married?'

'I have been divorced now longer than I was married. My daughter was nineteen in January, but I haven't seen her for the past fourteen years.'

Suddenly he poured out to her, a woman he hardly knew, the sad story of his daughter Ann's disappearance from his life. And the way she listened to him, just looking at him with her serious, understanding eyes, and nodding, and asking questions now and again, made him as happy and relaxed as he could remember ever having been.

'Well, Mark, why don't you let bygones be bygones. You can't change your past, can you? And you can't force other people to act to your liking either. I'm sure your daughter will find you very soon herself. She's a grown-up girl now and she will have her own opinion about things and people. She might find you out of pure curiosity. All you have to do is be ready for your meeting so that you don't disappoint her when you meet. If I were you, I would try to imagine how you will meet and what you will tell her about yourself. How you will share your memories of her childhood with her or tell her about her roots, about your parents and more distant ancestors. Then, instead of suffering depression every time you think of your daughter, you'll have a positive image of what might happen in the future when you meet.'

'If we meet, Sofia.'

'No "ifs", Mark, it will happen, definitely!' Her enthusiasm, the way she eagerly and openheartedly responded to his troubles was amazing. But it was time to go back to the office.

'Can we meet tonight? I would like to invite you for dinner, Sofia.'

'Well, thank you, Mark, I don't really know. The thing is, I'm not sure it is safe to go out at night. Would you like to come to my place? I promise to feed you.'

'Thank you very much. By the way, I could cook. Have you ever tried roast beef and Yorkshire pudding?'

'Yorkshire pudding? Never even heard of it. Could chicken replace beef in your recipe?'

Mark would not mind replacing every single thing as long as Sofia was going to be there, especially now that their brief acquaintance seemed to be developing into a close friendship. They decided that Sofia would pick him up from his hotel on her way home.

Back in her office, Sofia tried to concentrate on the handout material for the next dental factory project meeting, but gave up after a number of attempts. She decided she would finish it first thing on Monday morning. Then she phoned home and told granny that they were having a visitor that evening.

'What do you want me to do, apart from washing behind my ears?' asked granny.

'That will be it, gran. Why don't you teach Yashka some English words? Our guest is British.'

'Is he? Well, that's very, very interesting.'

Sofia noted that there was something strange in grandma's intonation. Probably because it was a long time since a stranger had passed through their door.

'She must be bored,' thought Sofia.

Mark was waiting for her outside the hotel with a bag in his hand.

'Don't worry, I'm not moving into your house yet. I had time to kill, so I went to the market and bought some beef and a couple of other things. I hope your chicken won't mind if we don't eat it tonight.'

'No, it will be all right. Speaking of birds, we have a small green parrot as a member of the family. He can maintain a conversation, but only in French. My grandmother taught him some words she still remembers.'

'Oh, I see. Am I meeting any other members of the family tonight apart from your English-speaking daughters, French-speaking nana and the parrot?'

'Actually, you might. Lisa is always bringing home forlorn kittens or other injured animals. Last month it was a crow with a broken wing. Turned out to be a terrible thief. Yashka, the parrot, didn't like her either. We were both glad when she recovered and flew away.'

They were chatting all the way to Sofia's house, touching on insignificant subjects only. It seemed to Mark that spending a winter in Karaganda had taught him to have a more casual attitude towards visiting other people's houses. Most Russians lived more openly than his compatriots at home. He could hardly imagine doing the same thing in the UK: having met someone two days ago and offering to cook a meal for them and their family in their own home! Had Russia changed him or was it Sofia's easy ways that made him do it? He didn't care. He was happy and looking forward to spending some time with Sofia again, seeing her house and meeting her family.

The evening turned out to be a real success. They laughed a lot together from the start. Following Mark's brief introduction to the old lady and the girls, he was led by Sofia straightaway to the small kitchen and had a floral printed apron put on him. Sofia's grandmother was absolutely shocked at such a welcome and tried to explain to Mark, gesticulating and using French words, that it was not the way she had taught her granddaughter to treat her guests.

'Don't you worry, granny. Mark has even brought his own food to cook,' Sofia commented, when he opened his bag and took out a piece of beef, a bottle of red wine and a box of chocolates.

'What vegetables do you need to go with your beef, Mark? I've got some potatoes, cabbage, a tin of peas. Will that be enough?'

'Absolutely fine. I also need some milk, eggs and flour for the Yorkshire puddings. Please show me what kind of baking tins you have.' In no time the beef was in the oven, vegetables were selected and ready for peeling. They opened the bottle of wine accompanied by a tin of olives and small pieces of toast with caviar, prepared by Alexandra while Mark was busy with the beef. A pleasant conversation was going on, mixing the languages: English and Russian, some of granny's French. Sofia and Alexandra translated for granny. At some point granny asked Lisa to bring the album with the family photographs.

'Sorry, Mark, I know how boring it is to look at somebody's old photographs, full of people you have never met,' said Sofia, 'but do you mind having a look, just to please gran? Her album is so old it's more a collector's item than family snaps.'

Mark didn't mind at all. They cleared the end of the table and Alexandra put in front of him a large dark green faux leather album. It was decorated with printed irises in the Art Nouveau style and faded at the edges. His hostesses were discussing the salad ingredients. Mark opened the album, browsing through it page by page. It was interesting. There was a young Russian priest with a beard on a distinguished face. Beside him was a small, pretty lady, probably his wife. In another picture the same couple, but older, were surrounded by six children, three boys and three girls. Then the same boys and girls, older, some of them in school uniform. Mark kept on turning the pages. Suddenly his attention was totally arrested by one of the pictures. He could hardly believe his eyes. His own granddad and uncle Steven dressed in Cossack uniforms with a young lady in fancy dress were looking at him from the photograph! It was a copy of the picture he had inherited from his granddad. Probably Mark made an odd noise or looked a bit strange. Sofia came up to him, worried.

'Are you all right Mark? Would you like another glass of wine? We'll be eating in half an hour. The starters are ready.'

'Please, Sofia, tell me who is the young lady in this picture?' asked Mark, embarrassed by his excitement.

'This one? It's granny Nadya, my grandmother's older sister. She was what you would now call a local socialite. She was fond of partying and dancing.'

'Do you know who the young men are with her?'

'Its amazing Mark, that you recognise your compatriots even in Cossack costumes. They were her English friends, William and Steven. William was more than just a friend.

There was a romance, interrupted by the Revolution. That's what I heard from granny Nadya, anyway.'

'You wouldn't believe it, Sofia! William was my grandfather, and I knew his friend Steven very well. Granddad was Scottish by the way.'

'Are you serious, Mark? You're not joking? Your own grandfather? I must tell gran.' She was speaking Russian with her grandmother for a while. Alexandra, who had left the kitchen by that time, overheard some excitement and joined them. Now all of them were as thrilled as he was. Grandmother crossed herself and hugged Mark. Then she sat down in front of him, brushing away her tears and looking at him as if trying to find his grandfather's features in Mark's face. Sofia translated for him:

'She says she met your grandfather only once, when visiting her sister in Grozny.'

'Please ask your grandmother to tell me all about it. I have a confession to make, Sofia, dear. My business trip wasn't the main reason for visiting Grozny. I was hoping to find some traces of granddad's life here. Sorry I didn't tell you before. I was afraid you would think it was crazy, chasing my childhood memories like this.'

'There's no need to apologise, Mark. You wouldn't tell your family secrets to a total stranger. Anyway let's listen to what granny has to tell us.'

She started her narration, giving Sofia time to find the exact words in English:

It was my last Easter holiday at home before graduation. My older sister Nadya had already been teaching in Grozny for two years. When father said he had some business in town we all thought just as well, he could bring Nadya back home for Easter. I was glad when I was allowed to accompany him on this trip. The night before I was, as

91

always, too excited to sleep. Everyone in the family knew about that peculiarity of mine and mother told Shura, our middle sister, who shared the bedroom with me:

'If Asya keeps stirring in her bed all night she won't be allowed to go. Do you hear me, Asya? There is nothing to worry about. Father Dimitriy from Nikolaevskaya is going with you too. Your picnic basket is ready in the kitchen. I will wake you at dawn. Please relax my darling. Good night, God bless you.'

She kissed and crossed me. I tried to do my best, squeezing my eyelids tightly, lying straight in my bed till my body was numb and my eyes sore, but sleep would not come to me. Thousands of possibilities of what might go wrong and spoil the adventure were racing round in my head. For instance, our carriage might suddenly break down or one of the horses might start limping. Had they remembered to put salt and pepper in the picnic basket? They forgot it last time. Silly thoughts like these kept me awake. When I saw the sky in the frame of the window becoming grey against the dark wall, I thought, 'Oh, thank God, it's morning at last,' and slipped away into a sweet relaxing dream. The next moment Shura's voice said,

'Hey, who's the member of the big expedition here? Rise and shine! Do you know you've been talking in your sleep? Something about salt and pepper.'

I was ready in no time. Mother wouldn't let me go without breakfast, which I secretly shared with Vasiliy, the cat. Then I took my hat and coat and another compulsory item, galoshes, black rubber overshoes, which were specially equipped with long shoelaces. At that time Grozny was notorious for its muddy streets. The town was built in a hollow between the mountains. The clayish soil held the rainwater for ages. That extraordinary mud was

92

dense and sticky. It would catch the soles of your shoes, so the only way to walk was by twisting your feet with every step, the way people dance nowadays.

'Nobody is twisting now, granny. They did that in the sixties,' Alexandra interrupted the story. 'And didn't you have such things as pavements then?'

Granny continued:

Yes, there were cobbled roads and wooden pavements in the centre, but unfortunately they never met. So, whenever you needed to cross the street you had to do your ritual dance. That's why when we went to the town we always had a pair of galoshes with us, even in summer, because the clayish mud puddles dried very slowly. We fastened our galoshes tightly with the shoelaces. I am going into every boring detail, because those galoshes played a very important part in our story. So we started out early and arrived in the town at noon. First of all, we picked up Nadya from her school. She looked lovely. I was very proud that this pretty young lady was my own sister.

'There's something I want to ask you, father,' Nadya said straightaway. 'Would you mind if I didn't come home with you today? I have received an invitation to an Easter Ball in town. Father Alexei of the Archangel Michael church is taking his daughters. He said I could join them.'

'No, I don't mind at all, my dear. I'm going to see Father Alexei at the council today. It's very kind of him. I shall thank him. In that case let's have lunch together when my meeting is over.'

Then father drove us to the office of the Church council. Nadya and I decided to go for a stroll while he was busy.

'Please girls don't go far. And you, Asya, don't forget to put your galoshes on,' father said just in time before I jumped out of the carriage in my new boots.

I quickly fastened my galoshes and off we went. Almost every other house in the central Dvoryanskaya Street was a shop. They mostly sold fabrics, shoes or clothes. On the other side of the street there were food shops, like the butchers, the bakery, the dairy. In the window of the dairy there was a notice: "Ice-cream sold here".

'Look, Nadya, ice-cream! Let's buy some.' We ran across the street. The road wasn't bad, but there were some muddy patches. Nadya managed to cross safely, avoiding them. I rushed after her, too busy looking elsewhere, and suddenly one of my shoelaces came loose. The next moment, stepping on to the pavement, I felt that one foot was lighter than the other. Looking back, I saw my left galosh stuck firmly in the middle of the puddle. At this awkward moment I saw two young men leaving the dairy shop each carrying a tub of ice cream. They both looked unusual. Now I can say they looked foreign. At that time I had never met a foreigner. Our teacher of French and Good Manners, Madame Voizin, and our German pharmacist didn't count. They had both lived in Russia for God knows how long. But those two young men looked so different. First of all they were wearing long rubber boots over their smart riding breeches. Their tweed jackets were well cut. And their caps! I had never seen anything like those caps before. In fact I had probably never seen a cap before. All the men I knew wore either hats or Cossack fleece hats in winter. Nadya was standing facing me and couldn't see them. She was laughing and I, who a moment before was ready to burst into tears, started laughing too. You laugh very easily when you are young, don't you? The foreigners stopped. One of them passed his ice cream to his friend, stepped into the puddle, lifted my galosh out and handed it to me. I probably blushed all over, I suddenly felt very hot. He said something in a language I didn't understand. I murmured my *grand merci* with clumsy courtesy. Nadya did the same but in a very elegant way with her charming smile showing her beautiful even teeth. We rushed into the shop where the lady, who had seen the whole scene from the window, took me into the kitchen to wash my galosh. She told us that the foreigners we had just met were English engineers working at the new oil refinery plant. They had recently come from Baku and visited the town occasionally. That was all she knew about them.

I begged Nadya not to mention the episode to father, and especially to our brothers, because I didn't want to become a laughing stock for the rest of my holidays, and she promised she wouldn't.

That was the first and last time I saw your grandfather and his friend, Mark. The rest of this sad love story I know from what I overheard Nadya telling Shura and from what she bitterly told me many years later, when her romance had become only a sweet memory from the past. Nadya came home as she promised, the next day, after the Easter Ball. I saw that she was desperate for a *tête-à-tête* with Shura and I made a nuisance of myself, following them everywhere, mostly because I was afraid that Nadya would tell Shura about my fiasco with the galoshes. So when mother sent Shura to bring some root vegetables for borsch and Nadya said she would help her, I tiptoed down to the cellar after them. I quickly found myself a hiding place behind the big barrel of pickled cabbage and sat listening.

'Shurochka, I need to tell you, I think I've met the love of my life.'

'What? Again?'

'Oh, please, please don't laugh! It's serious this time.'

'Nadya my dear, can you talk so that you make some sense? Who is the Romeo? Where did you meet him?'

'Well, his name is William. William Stuart. He is an oil engineer from Great Britain.'

'An Englishman?'

'He is actually from Scotland. I met him at the Easter Ball. There were some other foreigners too. He was with his friend Steven Jones. I briefly saw them in town once before. Shurochka, he is so handsome and there is a kind of tenderness about him... And how clever he is!'

'How would you know? You don't speak his language, do you?'

'Oh, he speaks a little bit of French.'

'You are not fluent in French as far as I know, Nadya.'

'He said he was going to take some Russian lessons and asked me to teach him.'

'Fantastic idea, Nadyusha. You know the best remedy for love at first sight.'

'What is it?'

'Have a good second look.'

'Thank you my dear little sister. You're so sensible. If there were flies here they would die of boredom.'

'I mustn't upset the family. Listen, my Juliet, we'd better take these vegetables and run upstairs before mother sends Asya after us.'

I quickly made it up the stairs, frightened they would discover me spying on them. I was very pleased with Nadya. Whatever the business with the Scotsman was, she never mentioned my miserable galosh.

I was only a teenager, you know. I was very much absorbed in my own feelings and discoveries. Nadya and I had never been too close, probably because of the age gap. The sad end of Nadya's romance, the whole intensity of it, became clear to me only many years later. In the late thirties before the Second World War, after many years of spinster life, Nadya agreed to marry a middle-aged Armenian doctor. He was a widower, a funny little man with an extraordinary sense of humour. Everyone adored him. When I went to Nadya's the night before the wedding to help her with the food for the reception, I found her sitting on the floor in front of the fire, burning something and crying bitterly.

'What's wrong, Nadyusha? Why are you upset? You're not changing your mind, are you?'

'No, Asya, I'm not. That's why I'm burning the keepsakes of the love of my life, my dearest Scotsman. You remember him, don't you? The young gentleman who once rescued your galosh? You never knew that episode had a continuation, did you?'

'I actually did know you met him once after that, at the Easter Ball. I was hiding in the cellar when you were confiding in Shura. Strange that I should remember it after so many years. The memories of those last happy years before the Revolution! They have become a sort of keepsake in themselves. Everyone was alive: Misha, Zhora, father. The world seemed such a safe place.'

'I know.'

I was sitting there next to her watching the tongues of fire licking the yellowish pages of the old letters. Then I saw the photograph, the one you've seen in my album, and I put it in my pocket.

'Please let me take this one, Nadya. I promise to keep it safe where nobody will see it.'

'Asya I'm doing this for my own sake only. I know all the letters by heart anyway. Most of them were sent

97

from Baku, where William used to go on business trips. Some were from Berlin and some from London. This is the note he left in my letterbox. And this is his exercise book, where he was practising the Russian alphabet.'

'Did he study Russian?'

'He tried. That was how it all started. When we met at the ball he asked me if I could give him lessons. He had been too busy for regular classes. And we both knew they were an excuse for seeing each other before we started dating. The picture you want was taken in Christmas week when we were on our way to the fancy dress ball. By that time William and I were already secretly engaged.'

'But why was it such a secret, Nadya? I don't understand. You could have introduced him to us. You know our parents' house was always open for all our friends.'

'Oh, now I know it was silly. All that secrecy! But we were young and romantic. Besides, William wanted to make some financial arrangement. He was what you call "a self-made man". It was very important to him to be able to tell my father that he could support a wife. He planned that we should spend our honeymoon in Paris, then visit Scotland. Oh, we planned everything years in advance. What we never imagined was that revolution and civil war would leave all our plans in ruins.'

'So where was William when the Reds arrested father and threw us out of the house? When we came to the town to you?'

'I had had no idea where he was for quite a while by that time. And I never saw him again. Twice I had scraps of paper from him, passed on by unknown people. After father's arrest I was so scared for you. You know what could have happened to all of us if the Bolsheviks knew I had "a contact abroad". So when an opportunity came to send him a message, I wrote to say that it was all over between us. I had to. And I am pleased I did. At least you all survived. Father came back from the labour camp. The children grew up at home, not in some communist orphanage.'

When they sat down for their dinner late that night Mark had already been accepted as a member of the family. The beef Mark cooked was probably not the best of his culinary achievements but the ladies complimented him on it anyway. The Yorkshire puddings were left for some other time. Sofia couldn't find the proper baking tins, and to tell the truth, all of them were too excited to be bothered.

Mark left Sofia's apartment at about eleven o'clock, which Sofia thought was late, and she asked him to call her as soon as he got back to the hotel, she wanted to be sure he had arrived safely. Before leaving, Mark received an invitation for Sunday lunch, but he hoped to see her the next day, Saturday, too. He was supposed to fly back to Karaganda on Sunday, but he was going to call his colleague Jack and ask for a delay.

Arriving back at his hotel, Mark was surprised to see a message from Jack, 'Get in touch with me ASAP'.

He dialled Jack's number, wondering what kind of emergency it could be.

'Mark, where the hell have you been? Can you change your flight to tomorrow? I really need you here. Martin was on the phone today, asking us both to fly back to Spain. So tomorrow is the last presentation and that is it. Back to civilisation! Fancy a nice celebratory dinner at the marina?'

'Hold on, Jack, why is it so sudden?'

'Well, he says we are sold out for now. What's your problem? I thought you would dance when I told you.'

'I wanted to stay in Grozny for a while. It's a family matter.'

'What? Already? Look, mate, I am only passing on the message. Why don't you come back over here, finish the business, and then call Martin and ask for some holiday? Would that make sense?'

'I suppose so. Okay, Jack, I'll try to change my flight tomorrow, but if I can't, I'll see you on Sunday.'

'What time are you back in Karaganda?'

'About six.'

'Okay, give me a ring when you know. Cheers.'

'Cheers, Jack'.

After that he called Sofia as he had promised. He knew she must be tired and didn't keep her long on the phone. He just asked if she could include him in her plans whatever she was doing the next day. He was tired himself even though it was still early for him. But he couldn't sleep. He stretched on his bed recalling the events of that amazing day. Lovely girls, all four of them. Grandma looked so fragile but what a memory! 'I wish I could remember what I did a month ago, let alone decades ago,' Mark thought, effortlessly falling asleep.

Saturday

He was dreaming of walking along a beach at sunrise. The sea was calm, the colour of liquid gold. He was walking towards a woman's figure outlined against the sky lighting up on the horizon. It was so far away he could hardly see it but somehow he was sure that it was Sofia. He started walking faster, then running, but couldn't get closer. 'Sofia, Sofia!' he cried, but his voice was weak and she couldn't hear him.

He woke up with his heart beating fast as if he had been really chasing somebody. It was still very early to call her. Mark got up, made a cup of instant coffee using his portable traveller's kit, lit a cigarette and tried to make sense of all the events of the past two days. They were logical enough if you looked at them separately, but seemed absolutely surreal taken all together. Now he believed he had been attracted to Sofia straightaway because he had subconsciously recognised her family features, so familiar from the old photograph.

He was sipping his coffee, smiling in anticipation of everything that life was going to open up for him from now on. He was planning his next visit to Grozny in a very short time. He was also hoping that Sofia would come to Spain. They would have plenty of time to get to know each other better. Suddenly his life wasn't spent or useless any more. He was in love.

At nine o'clock Mark, bathed, shaven and dressed in freshly ironed clothes, dialled Sofia's number, unable to wait any longer.

'Ahlo?' she answered, her lovely voice was sleepy.

'Morning, Sofia. Were you asleep?'

'Hello, Mark, not any more.'

'Sorry to wake you up.'

'No, it's okay, I've plenty of things to do today. We stayed up late yesterday after you left, discussing the surprises of life. Anyway, Mark, are you free to give me a hand today?'

'Yes, of course, Sofia. What do you want me to do?'

Sofia wanted him to join in her preparations for tomorrow's lunch. She suggested they meet at the hotel entrance. She was going to finish her shopping. Then they would take the bags home and do "the touristy bit", as she had promised. The rest of the day had not yet been planned.

'Never mind what we're doing, Sofia, I'm happy to be around.'

'Okay. So see you in about an hour, Mark.'

Half an hour later Mark was already standing on the steps of the hotel watching both sides of the road and the pavement in front of him. He had decided that he would run down the steps to meet her and kiss her on her cheek very casually, before taking her hand ready to stroll along to wherever they were going. But when he actually saw her, so young and fresh in her weekend gear, jeans and jacket, a blue knitted scarf round her neck, he just stood there looking at her coming up to him. When he saw her beautiful greenish eyes closely, he just uttered a weak 'Hello'.

Actually, if he had wanted to show his feelings he couldn't have done better. Sofia read his expression to her total satisfaction and was touched. She had not admitted it to herself yet, but her long spell of being single was over. She felt sexy, flirty and ready for an adventure.

Two things prevented Mark from recognizing Sofia's

feelings. On the one hand, he was too overwhelmed by his own feelings and on the other afraid of spoiling their growing intimacy. The most surprising discovery he made was that he was happy just to walk next to her listening to that musical voice of hers or catching a glimpse of her smile, the look of her shining eyes, sensing the rhythm of her short steps beside him.

'Listen, Mark, I've changed my initial plan. We're not going to the market. I was lucky, the small market across the road from where I live was open so all my shopping is done. Now we can take advantage of this nice weather and go for a walk. I'm going to show you one of the local historical places which is just round the corner.'

They crossed the square with Lenin's monument in the centre. The monument was too big for a small square. Passing a small, neat looking garden, they went on to a quiet street. Sofia brought Mark to a short stone wall between two buildings. The wall looked like an imitation of an entrance with a thick iron door in the middle. On one side of the door there was a bust of a man. His epaulettes indicated a nineteenth-century military background. On the other side there was a commemorative marble plaque.

'This is a very modest memorial to one of the most courageous and skilful military commanders of the nineteenth century in Russia, General Yermolov. As you see, it is not a piece of art at all. Very much in the tradition of socialist realism, the general trend in Soviet art,' Sofia said. She continued her lecture: 'Nobody paid any special attention to this place – another dusty item of long-forgotten history, until one day in the nineteen sixties the neighbourhood was awakened by an explosion. The bust was shattered into small pieces. So were the windows in the nearby house. I remember it because most of my classmates lived in this area. Everyone was talking about it the next day at school. The boy whose windows were broken became a kind of celebrity. He was asked to tell how it had happened again and again by the pupils and even the teachers. After classes we were all running over here to have a look. But the place had already been cleaned up and was guarded by militia. There was no official explanation for the blast, but somehow everyone knew. It was revenge. Chechens had done it. The famous General had been the chief commander of the Russian army that had conquered them in the eighteen-hundreds.

'He must have been very displeased with the local population, because in his report to Tsar Alexander 1 he had written something like: "The nation (meaning the Chechens) is not able to be corrected or improved, needs to be destroyed." A very cruel statement of course. I wonder if he did write that? There were some facts in his life contradicting it. In the local picture gallery, where I'm going to take you now, you'll see the works of the first Chechen artist, Zakharov. A very talented artist. He was an orphan, found and brought up by General Yermolov. He gave the gifted boy the best education in fine arts available at that time, sent him to the Saint-Petersburg Fine Arts Academy and then to Italy.'

'Well, who knows now how it was in reality. What happened to the bust after the explosion? Is this a restored one?' Mark asked.

'There were rumours that the KGB ordered enough busts to fill a spacious cellar under the memorial, ready for replacement if anyone wanted to repeat the attempt.'

'Did they try it again?'

'I'm not sure. I think they did. At least once. But the

first explosion was like a declaration – the Chechens were resuming the fight for independence inherited from their ancestors. You see, it seemed as if the Russians had inherited all the colonial hatred felt towards the former Russian Empire. Do you see here any parallels with the British Empire and its colonial politics?'

'Well, I suppose so. But we live in different times. The world has changed a few times since then. It's not your fault or mine that some generals were cruel to other people!'

'This is what you think. I'm not sure everyone over here shares your views. It's a very sore point for Chechens, and could easily be used to start serious trouble.'

'Like war?'

'No, no, they are too clever to bring it all to war. They are survivors, the Chechens. I am sure they understand it could destroy them as a nation.'

Now they were on their way back to Lenin Square, passing the garden again.

'Let's find a bench in the sun. You can have a cigarette and I'll go on lecturing,' Sofia said.

'I was about to suggest it,' Mark answered and they found themselves a bench.

'Now, Mark, I have to tell you, apart from putting you in the picture purely historically, there are some other points. We've already touched on the subject of your coming over to Chechnya during this time of political change. We were discussing the possibility of your starting a business in Grozny. It's my duty to warn you of the danger we might face here.'

'Danger? What kind of danger and for whom? Are you personally in any danger?'

'No, Mark, I'm not. But it's not the best time to start a

business. Anyway, being an optimist, I believe it will soon be over.'

'You know, dear, after four months in Kazakhstan, I have some knowledge of what's going on in this country. But on the other hand I'm only here thanks to the political changes. So you see I've become an optimist, too. When we started in Karaganda I was very much concerned that the whole idea was a mistake. Life proved that I was wrong.'

Having said that the local population wasn't in any danger, Sofia knew that she was lying. Why hadn't she told him the truth? she asked herself many times later on. It was because of her damn pride. She didn't want to show a man she hardly knew, especially a foreigner, that she was vulnerable and insecure. She wouldn't expose her weakness. At least not just then.

'Did you have any breakfast this morning, Mark?'

'No.'

'Neither did I. There is a café across the road called *Arfa*. Let's see if it's open before we starve to death.'

The café was almost empty. Sofia chose some hot flat cakes and tea for their breakfast.

'This café specialises in Chechen cuisine. These pancakes are called *chepelgash*. Look, they are stuffed. These are with cottage cheese and then we'll have some with creamed pumpkin.'

'Umm, it's delicious!'

They must have been hungry because the cheesey pancakes were finished in no time.

While they were waiting for the pumpkin ones, Mark decided it was a good moment to bring up the subject of his next visit to Grozny.

'Sofia, you know I have to go back to Karaganda

tomorrow. I had hoped I could stay longer, but for some reason my boss wishes to wrap up the business at very short notice. It doesn't matter actually. I've already decided to come back over here as soon as I can.'

'And when will that be?'

'Well, it shouldn't take more than a couple of days, a week at the most. Can I ask you to book a hotel for me, Sofia?

'Sure. Just ring me.'

'You know I loathe the thought of having to go back now when we have just started ...,' Mark went on, suddenly hesitating, '... to get to know each other. But we'll have plenty of time ahead of us, won't we?'

'Oh, yes, I suppose so. We can try to find more information on your grandfather and probably some partners for your business.'

'Yes, of course ...' He wanted to tell her that he had a better reason for coming back, that he was head over heels in love with her, but at that moment another portion of pancakes arrived. And after the interruption he thought it might be better to keep his feelings to himself this time. After all, he would be back in a week and could stay long enough to start a serious relationship.

When they had finished their breakfast, Sofia went on with her tour, taking him to the picture gallery and the local museum of history and geography.

The day lived up to their expectations totally. They had another meal together, shared a bottle of wine. From time to time their hands were touching and aching for another touch. When their eyes met there was a hidden question in his, 'Is it possible? Can we? Can we now?' And he was pretty sure that the answer was, 'Yes.'

In the ladies room, Sofia looked into a hazy mirror

pressing her palms against her blushing cheeks. 'Like a teenage girl,' she thought. But she was not a girl. She was a woman who had experienced two broken marriages. She was seriously afraid of being hurt again. 'No,' she decided. 'He is nice and I do like him a lot. And I must be honest, I do want to go to bed with him. But not tonight. I'd better wait until he comes back, *if* he comes back.'

Their parting that night was easy and full of hidden promise. They were going to see each other the next day. Sofia suggested that Mark should check out at about ten o'clock and come to her place with his suitcase. The other guests would join them at twelve, so they could all have lunch together. She had already asked one of her guests to give Mark a lift to the airport, which was not more than twenty minutes' drive away. Mark thought she definitely had a special touch when it came to making arrangements and organising things in the most appropriate way.

Back home, Sofia went to bed early, pretending she was tired, but she lay on her sofa-bed, staring into the darkness and thinking of Mark, of his grandfather and Nadya. 'Lucky me, meeting Mark in better times. At least nothing can interfere with our relationship. It will be our choice only,' Sofia thought. Then she tried to picture Mark's face, but the image kept slipping away from her now sleepy mind. Suddenly it was a recollection of his smell that came back to her: a mixture of freshly ironed cotton shirt, the fragrance of his aftershave and something else that she was unable to identify, but that made her whole body ache for his closeness.

Sunday

'Guests, guests! We are having guests today!' It was the first thought that came into Alexandra's head as soon as she opened her eyes. Even before she opened the curtains in the bedroom she shared with Lisa and nana Asya, she felt sure that the day must be bright and sunny. She had grown up in a so-called "open house": grandma's and mother's students, her mum's girlfriends and her father's mates dropped in every day without special invitations. For as long as she could remember she had sat somewhere in a corner listening to mum talking to her girlfriends. Among the everyday topics of the latest season's fashions or affairs of the heart, they discussed new books, films, theatre performances, art exhibitions.

The best part of life was of course the parties with lots of preparations and much excitement. She and Lisa had always taken part in everything: first in decorating the flat and laying the table and then in cutting up vegetables for salads. They also helped mother with her baking. They liked their home parties not so much for the festive food, which was nice and tasty, but mostly for the atmosphere of a shared good time. The guests would tell jokes and dance and sing, accompanied by a guitar or two. Her father had been a good guitarist. She herself would risk playing a number on the piano. Lisa liked to show off with her ballet numbers. Aunty Mila, mother's school friend, would put up her "wall paper", a newsletter with satirical sketches and caricatures specially made for the event, somebody's birthday or a Soviet bank holiday.

That is why, by the time she was a teenager, Alexandra was fully aware of how things should be between people.

There were three simple rules: make friends only with people you like; share your interests with your friends; always be there for them for good or ill.

Things changed for Alexandra and Lisa when their parents got divorced. Two years spent in the far north of Russia with mum and her new husband was a totally new experience for them, but as soon as mother left him and they came back to Grozny everything was pretty much the same, except for the absence of their father, who now lived on the Kamchatka Peninsula in the Far East. Alexandra returned to her friends at school and was busy with her own intense relationships, but the circle of family friends remained close and enjoyable.

That morning she was looking forward to the introduction of their new acquaintance, the British man Mark, to the rest of them. She had already taken the old photograph from grandma's album to show when the amazing story was told. What she liked about her family was that life had never been boring. She knew the other girls envied her. She could hear her mother and grandma Asya were already up. Their voices and the clink of crockery coming from the kitchen made life feel cosy and stable. Would it be like that forever?

'Sashka!' her mother called her, 'Sleepyhead, breakfast is ready, come on, get up!' And she was already in the bedroom, bending over her, kissing and tickling her and pushing her out of bed till she felt annoyed and would have preferred to be left alone. When she jumped out of bed, and Lisa jumped out of hers mum ran away from them both and they ran after her because she had to be punished for her invasion. All three of them ended up on the lounge floor catching their breath, weak with laughter.

'Come on, girls, you have plenty of things to do'. That

was grandma's voice from the kitchen competing with a duo of Yashka the parrot and a popular singer from the radio. Sunday morning had started.

Mark arrived at about eleven. Sofia made him a mug of freshly brewed coffee. She prepared it in the Turkish way, popular in Russia, using a small long-handled pot. Mark remarked again, how very much at home he felt among them in their small, white kitchen. There was a smell of Christmas as it was in his childhood memories: roast turkey, cinnamon and vanilla.

'Are you roasting turkey, Sofia?' he asked.

'It's a goose. I was afraid a chicken might not be enough for the number of people I've invited today, so I thought it would be a good idea when I saw the bird at our local small market yesterday. But now I'm not sure about its age. Might come out a bit tough. Never mind, there is plenty of food.'

'You must have lots of friends.'

'I was born and spent most of my life in this town, except for the first five years and two years when I was in the Far North.'

'What did you do in the Far North?'

'Well, it was my second marriage. A big mistake.' Sofia's face suddenly changed its lovely cheerful expression. Mark realised how the absence of a smile gave her face the determined look of a pagan goddess. Probably the trick was in her very dark eyebrows contrasting with her light eyes, changing their colour from green to grey.

'Sorry, I didn't mean to be nosey.'

'Oh, it's okay. You asked about my friends, Mark. Most of them you are going to meet today. My schoolmate, Mila is probably my most long-standing friend. She writes for a local paper. Her friend from her student days, Lena,

111

teaches Russian literature at the University. I first met Lena at Mila's when I was pregnant, so I have known her now for fifteen years. Larissa was my translator colleague from the Oil Research Institute, though I have known her since my student years. Of course it's not the number of years that matters. They have all been a part of my life as much as I've been a part of theirs, and they still are.'

'Can I also be a part of your life, Sofia? I mean, do something useful?'

'Yes, sure. Do you want to help Alexandra set the table? Sasha, Mark will help you to convert the table. She'll show you how to do it, Mark.'

They were nearly through with the table when the bell rang and Mark was introduced to a redheaded and loud Larissa accompanied by her eleven-year-old daughter Veronika, or Nikushya as everyone called her, and a boyfriend, Sergei. Larissa's English was as good as Sofia's. As Alexandra couldn't wait any longer to tell the newcomers about the connection between Mark's grandfather and their family, Sofia let her do the talking, while she finished setting the table and asked Mark to open a bottle of wine.

The story had to be repeated several times that day: first, because the girls couldn't wait, and then because they wanted to enjoy their success again and again. Mark stayed at Sofia's place for a couple of hours, and left the party still in full swing with a doggy-bag wrapped by grandmother.

Everyone drank to his safe journey. He assured his new friends that he was going to be back soon. As Sofia had promised, Stas, one of the guests, took Mark to the airport on time. Stas hardly knew more than ten English words altogether. Mark's Russian vocabulary was about the same. But Mark was glad he didn't need to make conversation. He sat in the car looking at the road, his mind pleasantly fixed on the memory of Sofia's lips first touching his mouth and then parting willingly and hungrily, making his own blood strike him like a hot wave. What a wonderful moment! Mark had not expected Sofia to leave her guests, but she had gone down to see him to the car and that was where it had happened. He kissed her and she responded. She responded! Finish with all the formalities in Karaganda and fly back the very next day! Thank you grandpa! You should have sent me here long ago.

He flew back to Karaganda in a state of absolute happiness. The future was clear and bright like the sky in the plane's window.

Sofia retuned to her guests trying to hide the emotions stirred by their kiss, but she wasn't very good at pretending.

'At least you're the one who's happy nowadays, dear,' Vera said, coming up to her and putting her arm around her shoulders. 'And we are all happy for you. Your Englishman is cute and has definitely fallen for you. Let's drink to Sofia's future happiness with Mark, everyone!'

'Oh, you must be crazy, Verochka. We've only just met, you know.'

'Sofia, don't be silly. This is a chance for you to leave this place for good. He's not married, is he?'

'No, he's divorced, but you never know, maybe there's a woman in his life. It's hard to believe that there isn't.'

'We may assume that there was someone, but now that he has met you, Sonechka, there is hardly a chance for her. He is trapped! By you, our dear tigress!'

Nikolay joined the toast.

'Oh, sure. Look at them all, trapped! The whole terrace stuffed with cages.'

'Okay, okay, sorry, Sonia, I meant it as a compliment, but obviously only made a stupid remark. I'm a bit inadequate, I'm afraid.'

'Listen, guys. Nikolay and I have something to tell you,' said Nina, Nikolay's wife.

Everyone could easily guess what kind of announcement they were about to hear.

'You are leaving Grozny, aren't you, aunty Nina?' Alexandra voiced the question for them all.

'Yes, darling, we are. We've already made arrangements to sell our house. It's not a fair price, but at the moment nobody would give us more. You know what's going on. We were counting the removal vans driving through our district today. There was one in every other backyard. Chechens are buying the houses and flats for practically nothing.'

'Have you decided to move only recently? Why are you moving so quickly?' asked Larissa.

'Nikolay has found a job as a construction engineer in Krasnodar. They want him to start as soon as possible. We simply can't miss the chance.'

'Yes,' said Nikolay, 'the company has promised me two rooms in a hostel for us all at the moment, with the prospect of buying a flat in a building which is currently under construction in Krasnodar. Hopefully, the money we are getting for our house now will be enough to cover the first down payment for the flat.'

'Everyone is leaving. Look, there's a removal van over there, too', said Mila, who was having a cigarette at the window.

'It's the same thing round where I live,' said Vera. 'The

taxi driver, a Chechen, told me today, "We all have guns, but we are not going to shoot Russians, we're only going to shoot in the air to scare them away, like sparrows." Well. I was scared, listening to him. What will happen to us? What shall we do? My parents spent years building their house. It's a good brick house, you know, with all facilities, but the money they could get for it now wouldn't even give them the chance to buy a garden shed in Russia.'

Sofia knew the party, planned as a break from all their current problems, was over. She offered tea with honey cake. Most of her friends had a sweet tooth. Their attention was briefly drawn away from their problems, at least on the conversational level. At that moment Stas returned from the airport and joined them. He reported that the plane with Mark on board was in the air and Mark sent them all his love and a gigantic box of chocolates he had bought at the airport. Sofia opened the box. They all helped themselves, wishing Mark a good flight and making all kinds of comments about Russian girls having a soft spot for foreigners. Sofia laughed and told them to shut up or she would take the box away from the table. But she was glad to see them enjoying themselves again. She thanked Mark in her thoughts for giving them all a break they needed so badly.

Soon after tea Sofia's friends hurried to say goodbye before it got dark. Larissa stayed longer than the others to help with the washing up. They left Sergei, Larissa's new boyfriend, in the lounge watching a football match and they had a good girly chat in the kitchen. Granny tried to help them but Sofia asked her to leave the battle to them. The old lady had been in the kitchen since early morning and obviously needed a rest.

'Now, Lara, tell me at last what's going on with Sergei?' asked Sofia.

'I suppose it's not hard to guess. Sex, my dear. It's called sex.'

'Well, well, that's not so bad for a start.'

'Unfortunately for me, it's both a start and a finish. We enjoy each other's company, but there is no future in our relationship. We don't have bloody time, do we? He is responsible for his mother and two younger sisters. They are moving to Voronezh soon. He says it's the wrong time for him to make any commitments. So the only choice I have is either to stop seeing him right now or wait until he eventually disappears from my life ... like melting snow. Just a wet spot! A wet spot on my pillow.'

'What does your mother say? Where do you meet?'

'Oh, she doesn't know anything about it. She thinks we're only seeing each other. Well, you know, like holding hands. I've got the keys to my aunt's flat, the one who moved with her daughter to Vladikavkaz. They haven't sold the flat yet. It's only ten minutes' walk from my place, very convenient. By the way, when Mark is back I can give you the keys. I hope you'll need them.'

'Oh, I don't know.'

'Yes, you do. I have known you long enough to understand how you feel. You want him, don't you? Oh, look at you, you're blushing!'

'Yes, I must admit I am emotionally more involved with him, than I wanted to be. It's too soon, Lara. What if it's Mr. Wrong again?'

'Oh, don't be silly! Do we see any right ones around? I can tell you, my dear, I would already like to thank him for one simple thing: he has brought you back to life. I could hardly recognise you when you came back from the North, as if the opposite sex didn't exist at all. That's definitely not right!'

'Okay, okay. You've made your point.'

'Mum, mum, look', Veronika entered the kitchen with a picture she had drawn. It was a still life: two red apples in a wooden bowl and a wooden spoon next to it. 'Sasha made this composition for us to draw. But her picture is better than mine. Of course, her father has been teaching her.'

'It's a nice drawing, Nikusha. Are you going to colour it?' asked Larissa.

'Don't know, we haven't decided yet.'

'Whatever you do, you'd better be quick. We're going home in twenty minutes, half an hour at the most.'

'Oh, mum not in half an hour, please, I haven't seen Sasha for ages!'

'Sorry, darling, we have to. Your granny would worry herself to death if we were not back before dark, you know.' The girl ran out.

'Speaking of fathers, any news from your ex?' asked Larissa.

'Not much. His mother is not very well. Maybe he'll come to see her, I don't know. Neither Sasha nor Lisa seem to miss him much, or maybe they don't want me to know. And what about yours? Is he all right?'

'Got married recently. Can't believe anyone would want to marry that drunkard.'

'Maybe a woman with the same disposition for liquor?'

'Probably.'

'How are you ladies? Can I be of any help?' Sergei walked into the kitchen.

'No, thank you, Sergei, we've just finished. How was

117

the game?'

'Crap, actually. I'm not watching it any more, lost interest.'

'It's a shame, darling. Anyway we have to make a move' said Larissa.

Sofia and the girls saw them to the door, helping them on with their coats and making them a doggy-bag of honey cake and chocolates for their granny, Larissa's mother.

'Mum, he is nice, Sergei, isn't he?' Alexandra commented when the lift door closed taking their friends down.

'Well, I suppose he is. Why?'

'Nikusha said her mama really loves him. She always tries on different outfits when she's getting ready to meet him. And she's singing again when doing the chores about the house. Nikusha likes him too. She said he would make a good father.'

'Well, I really don't know, Sasha.'

The conversation became awkward for Sofia and she sighed with relief when it was interrupted by the telephone. It was Mark.

'The plane has just landed. I'm calling from the airport. How are you? Is the party still going on?'

'No, Larissa and her team have just left. They were the last to leave. Thank you for the chocolates, Mark. Couldn't you find a bigger box? This one will only last us till Christmas at our rate of consumption.'

'I thought it would be enough till the end of the week. And next week I will be back, bringing fruit from Kazakhstan. Grapes and melons are so good here you'll forget about chocolates.'

He wanted to add that sweetest of all were her lips, but the words seemed to be so trivial he didn't dare.

'Sofia, I will call you again from my apartment. Hopefully, I will know what's going on and when I can fly back to you.'

'Okay, Mark, I'll be waiting. Bye.'

'*Do svidanya*', said Mark in Russian.

But he never came back to Grozny and it was neither his fault nor his decision.

Memories, memories. They are like a frozen reflection of something that has been and gone. It is your choice to decide whether or not the reflection can be trusted. Where are the valleys kissed by the sun? Where is the green town of my childhood? The strong but fresh scent of lilac in spring followed by sweet and musky acacia blossom. The yellow pancakes of overripe apricots baking on the asphalt pavement as it melts in the heat. And in every season, overpowering all the fragrances and scents, is the smell of the oil refineries, their tanks and torches of burning natural gas a permanent part of the landscape. A monument to the courage of the firemen has become part of the city landscape, too. Not far from the monument was a beautiful park with a unique collection of roses. Hundreds of varieties blossomed from May till as late as November. Passing through the park on the way to my piano lessons, I used to make up stories to myself about the little fairy people living in the rose bushes. I even believed I had seen them a couple of times. My musical education turned out to be a disaster, but I can still distinguish traces of the fairies' wings in a Mozart symphony, and the outline of the old trees and shrubs of the park in a Bach fugue. Somewhere in the blue ocean above us in its full glory there floats a phantom town, created by the collective memories of its former citizens. It shines over the ruins, its houses and streets, smells and noises, imperishable as long as we live and keep our memories.

These memories are stored in a far corner of my heart. To bring them back is a luxury I can enjoy now only in rare moments of writing. My determination to produce some kind of historical analysis of the problems in Chechnya has been shaken, but has not totally disappeared. Unfortunately I don't have time for it now. Every day I need to draw on all my resources. But my reward is waiting for me at home in a rented one-room-and-a kitchen flat in the Davydkovo district of Moscow. They are all there, my daughters Alexandra and Lisa, my grandmother Anastasiya and Nelly, a little fluffy white mongrel. All alive, nobody in danger any more.

I have not mentioned Nelly before, so I must tell her story, too. It was soon after my party at which I had introduced Mark to my friends. Maybe that was a mistake because Mark disappeared from my life as suddenly as he had appeared in it. But nevertheless we had a nice time all together that day. So what about Mark? He phoned the next day.

'I'm very sorry, Sofia. I need to finish my business here. My employers insist we all go back to Spain at the end of the week, but my Russian visa will still be valid. I'll fly back to you. Or how about you coming to see me in Spain? What do you think?'

Marvellous! Absolutely wonderful! Right now I leave my family in the middle of I don't know what and go on holiday. I was furious. But then, I thought, it was my fault. I had lied to him about the whole thing, I had not given him a chance to understand the situation.

He was on the phone from Kazakhstan every day that week and then called twice from Spain. He promised he would come back soon, but he disappeared. I had been going to tell him about the danger we were in, but that would have been imposing on him. I was glad I had not told him: if he had disappeared because of that it would have spoiled the impression he had made and my memories

121

of those three happy days. These memories I do not keep locked away. I keep them handy like a purse. The purse is full of coins: silver of our words, gold of our silence.

Getting Ready to Leave
Grozny for Good

I need to return to the sequence of events. The jail riot happened less then a fortnight after the party. Was Nelly already with us? No, I think we found her shortly afterwards. After the riot, the darkness in the streets became even more terrifying. I usually dropped in after work to pick up Alexandra from school, only two streets away from home. Once on a miserable rainy afternoon Alexandra and I were passing through our yard, an area between three big tower blocks. It was planned originally as a park, but the trees and bushes were too young and very much neglected. Anyway, there were a few benches here and there, occupied by senior citizens on sunny days. That was where we saw it, the dog, a puppy really, a poor abandoned thing. It was not at all an unusual sight. People were moving for a better life, leaving their extra baggage behind. Grozny was full of stray cats and dogs.

'Mum, look.' She pointed to the dog. 'Let's take it home. We can't possibly leave it here, can we?'

'Sasha, what are you talking about? On the contrary, we can't possibly take on responsibility for another life, not now. You know perfectly well we must leave the town in the very near future. No, no, don't look at me like that. Yes, I am a cruel, heartless woman, I know.'

Our lift was out of order. And all the way to the sixth floor she tried to persuade me to take the dog. By the time we were home she was crying non-stop. I had rarely seen her in tears, even when she was a small child. Lisa certainly took her side. So, after a couple of hours of misery, when neither my arguments nor granny's helped, I gave up.

'All right, let's go down and check on the dog. If it's still there we'll take it in and then decide what we're going to do about it. Don't you think that it could have just been lost? Maybe the owners have found it already.'

Alexandra stopped crying and rushed downstairs at least ten steps in front of me. Lisa was hopping after her. The rain had stopped. There was no sign of the dog anywhere. We spent a peaceful evening watching Moscow programmes on television.

The next day, Alexandra finished school early in the afternoon. I knew she and Lisa would already be home by the time I got back from work. The lift was working, a nice surprise. I rang the bell. Alexandra opened the door, and I saw another surprise waiting for me there. It was next to her: washed and groomed, standing straight on its hind legs, keeping the front paws together, with a question in its clever black eyes. Or maybe it knew the answer well before my heart of stone melted and I uttered weakly:

'It's cute, isn't it?'

For my lack of opposition I was granted the privilege of giving the dog a name. My daughter, expert in veterinary matters, said it was a bitch so I decided that "Nelly" would suit that tiny, funny creature perfectly. Since then she has been with us through lots of things. And how she hates to see us packing!

After arriving in Moscow, we moved house practically every six months. The reasons varied, but were mainly because we couldn't afford the rising rent. I could not really blame our landlords. During the *perestroika* period renting out their flats became a business for Muscovites and was sometimes a family's only source of income. They would move the grandparents or parents, sometimes both, to live with them in their own small flats and then rent out the spare flat. Moscow became a new Babylon. All the fifteen former republics of the Soviet Union, that had vigorously sought political independence, were now going through enormous economic problems. The economic system of this giant country was probably not the best, but it did exist. Power stations, railways, even airlines, everything was shared. For example, cotton was grown in Kazakhstan but the mills were all in central Russia.

How did we end up in Moscow? It's a long story. I must return to my chronology: the first session of talks with the "dental Turk"; meeting Mark; the jail riot. That riot resulted in half the convicts miraculously escaping into the town through the militia cordons. Within a couple of days I was mugged on my own street. And it was not even dark. Getting off the tram, I didn't notice that all the other passengers had gone in other directions and I was the only one turning round the corner. Soon I noticed two tall men walking behind me along the street. The thought that they were actually following me did not cross my mind. I had a large working bag with me, more like a briefcase than a lady's handbag. It was very useful for office papers and daily shopping at the same time. One of the men grabbed my bag and started pulling it to himself, but I was holding it quite tightly. Then the other one struck me on the head with such force that I fell down on to the pavement. I let go of the handle of the bag and they started running away. I didn't feel any pain at that moment. What I felt was humiliation and fury. I jumped up and started running after them shouting: 'Help! Help! Militia! You bastards!' But, fortunately for me, they were running faster. That night I remember feeling an overwhelming, cosmic misery. Not only because I was sorry to lose the money which was in the bag and my Lancôme cosmetic kit, not even because one side of my face was burning and probably would be black and blue in the morning, but because the illusion of relative safety had gone. Even if we tried hard and played by the rules, like staying in after dark, and not interfering in the Chechens' political debates, we couldn't go on living like that.

Time to move. I phoned my boss and told him what had happened to me. He said it was the third such incident he had heard of in the past week. Next day he accompanied me to the militia station to make a statement. There was a queue of people who had all come for the same reason. At that time we were still doing what we would normally have done: going to the authorities hoping they would help. But chaos had started to spread through the town like some malignant tumour. At work we had a short but very important meeting. The manager asked if I was ready to move to the Russian town of Orel when our current work on the dental factory project was finished. Of course my answer was positive.

I am trying to remember if I thought of Mark at all. It seems strange, but I actually don't think I did. Not like now. I need only close my eyes to see his face. The expression of admiration and love in his eyes that morning, when I was approaching him and he was waiting for me on the steps of the hotel. It's so sentimental and probably all my fantasy, but I don't care.

New Prospects

That whole week we were busy drawing up the final version of the dental contract. The team of specialists would pass me prepared clauses in Russian, and then it was my turn. I translated them, faxed them to Turkey and on receiving the comments faxed back to me, I passed them to the team. And then we went through the whole process again. At last both sides were happy with the papers and a meeting was arranged for the following Monday. Our Turkish business partner expressed a wish to arrive on Saturday afternoon and spend a weekend in Grozny so we were rushing to organise his leisure time, too. Alexei, the manager, suggested a barbeque at his *dacha*, a summer country house. He asked me to help his wife Lilya in planning the party, and I ended up baking *pirozhki* and preparing the vegetables. Meat for the *shashlyk*, a Caucasian kebab, had been delivered in a quantity sufficient to feed a whole Turkish village. By the end of the day we were absolutely worn out. Alexei suggested that I take a morning off and then join them for the barbeque at noon.

The next day I enjoyed a lie-in till ten and a lazy breakfast with granny (Alexandra and Lisa were at school) and at half past eleven was ready to be collected. It was twelve already but there was still neither a car nor a phone call from Alexei. It wasn't like him at all. I was worried. Half an hour later Lilya was on the phone:

'Sofia, my dear, something terrible happened this

morning. Alexei asked me to call and tell you. Yaranov, the chief dentist, was shot in the street when he was leaving his office. The Turk is on his way to the airport, rushing back to Turkey. Alexei has gone to see him off.' She was crying. 'I am so, so scared! Please, come and see us at home tomorrow morning. You will, won't you? We must make arrangements to move as soon as possible.'

Needless to say, I was scared too. And I felt very sorry for Yaranov. Who had shot him, and why?

At nine o'clock the next morning I was sitting with Alexei and Liza in their kitchen over a cup of coffee working on our moving strategy. We agreed to go to Moscow and apply at the Ministry to re-register our company in Orel. After that we would take a night train to Orel and make all the arrangements there. This would include meeting the local authorities and getting all the required signatures and stamps. Then we would come back to Grozny and make arrangements to close the company.

Alexei did not tell me a lot about why Yaranov had been killed. The official explanation was a family vengeance. It was strange, but not at all impossible. There was another version. He didn't mention it, but I guessed. It was possible that, in trading refinery products, Yaranov had encroached on someone else's territory and he was being punished for that.

From the beginning, everything went according to plan. We managed to cover the whole business in Moscow and Orel in record time, in just three days. Alexei had friends in the Ministry. They knew about our circumstances and were very helpful and sympathetic.

Back in Grozny, we found a note on our office door stating that the company equipment had been seized and the manager would be seen by the authorities.

By that time we had a new government in Chechnya. The separatists had won the elections. Considering that military power had been in their hands before the elections, this was a rather predictable result. When Alexei headed for the appointment, I stayed with Lilya, who was afraid she might never see her husband again. However, he came back safe and sound with the news that the company had been closed down as a Russian espionage organisation. The problem lay in the name of the company, the "Russian Federation International Consulting Service", the two words "Russian Federation" automatically triggered suspicion. There was no chance of getting back our equipment. Welcome to the world of the absurd! Alexei was officially under investigation. He had been warned not to leave the town until it was resolved. Lilya poured us some cognac from her special reserves.

'Sofia, I am afraid you'll have to deal with the registration procedure in Orel on your own. We really can't afford to waste time. You have the list of offices we need to cover.'

'Fine, I can do that. But what shall we do after the registration? We had a reliable pool of customers here in Grozny. Who knows us in Orel?'

'Well, to begin with, the fact that we are formally registered with the Ministry of Foreign Affairs of the Russian Federation will give us some credibility with the local authorities.'

'Yes, Alexei. But forgive me, I still don't see sleepy provincial Orel as a centre of international business activity.'

'This was another point I planned to discuss with you today, Sofia.'

'Did you? Do I need another sip of cognac before you start?'

'You might. Now listen. Whatever you think of Orel, in Soviet times it was a small but busy industrial town with lots of factories and plants. Now most of them are dying. Since the disintegration of the Soviet Union they no longer have access to raw materials. Can you see my point? They have production sites, a workforce, even modern equipment. If we could come up with a project that would bring some of them back to life, we would soon be in business ourselves.'

'All right. But do you have any particular branch of business in mind?'

'Very much so. You have experience working in Joint Venture. If with your help we could bring in a foreign investor and start with the same kind of assembly lines you had in Grozny ...'.

'Oh, yes, I see now what you have in mind. I think it's a practical idea. I've kept in touch with some of the former partners, and it won't be a problem at all to find the others.'

'I'm glad we've come to an agreement. Let's now think it all through and come up with an offer as soon as the registration is completed.'

That's how I became a courier between Grozny, Moscow and Orel for the next couple of months. For me anything was better than waiting for the next nasty surprise. And I would almost have enjoyed my trips if it were not for the growing danger in Chechnya. The airline between Grozny and Moscow was closed. The only way to get to Moscow was by rail. There were rumours that trains going through the territory of the rebellious republic were sometimes stopped and robbed by gangs. I had to take a train every two or three weeks, playing Russian Roulette, pretending I was not troubled by the rumours. Usually I stayed overnight in Moscow with my second cousin Ella and then took the first train to Orel, spending another six or seven hours on the journey.

There was another mission for me to accomplish. Since Russia had started its economic blockade of Chechnya, state pensions had been paid irregularly and then had stopped altogether. The local authorities explained that the banks did not have enough cash reserves. There was only one way to deal with the situation. You could put in an order at the local post office and transfer your pension to any post office in Russia. I would usually carry four or five pension orders to Orel. I could not even think of refusing my old neighbours or granny's friends. I knew they would starve if I did. That meant I would return literally loaded with cash. Keeping in mind the possibility of encountering gangs, or just an ordinary mugger, I did not carry the money in my bag. There were several ways of doing it, the most common one being on my body. I stuffed the money into a stocking and tied it round my waist. Then I would put on a loose top to cover it up. Another way was to hide the money in a thermos flask, between the plastic shell and the glass container. Nobody would be suspicious if you had a flask of coffee with you on a long trip. The worst part of my escapades was that my family was fully aware that I was in danger. It took the train thirty-six hours to cover the distance between Grozny and Moscow. They waited for my call from Moscow, praying I was safe. My return trip with money worried them even more. Nelly, the new member of our family, became a comfort for us all in those days. But even she somehow knew the days of my departure in advance. She would refuse to play and would sit next to me watching me with her sad black eyes. It is only now, when we have been settled in Moscow for a while, that I can see how damaging that time of fear was for all of us, especially for Alexandra.

In my journeys back and forth, the short stay in Moscow was a real breath of fresh air. Russians from all the distant provinces of the old Empire, and of the Soviet Union which came after it, either adored or strongly disliked their capital: it depended on the way you saw the city. If you were on a short stay on your way to the other end of the enormous country, coming out on to the crowded station, making your way through the crowded metro to the equally crowded shopping malls was undoubtedly a nightmare. Even so, the heart of every citizen of the country, not necessarily Russian born, would beat faster at the famous view of the Kremlin and the Cathedral of Vasiliy Blazhenniy on Red Square. And if you looked at Moscow, as described by our poet and song-writer Bulat Okudzhava, "through the prism of history, prism of music, prism of love…", your every visit would be full of new revelations. Moscow would take you to her big Russian heart and open the doors of the best theatres, concert halls and art exhibitions in the world. It sounds like an extract from a guidebook, but it's true. That was what I tried to experience each time I visited. My cousin Ella was working as an administrator in one of the big film studios of Mosfilm. Mingling with the bohemian crowd was part of her life, and I joined her whenever I could.

Moscow was full of opportunities and not only in its cultural life. The Russian market had become a powerful new attraction for foreign businesses. That meant there must be opportunities for me to find work.

'Forget your sleepy Orel. Your place is here, in Moscow,' Ella tried to convince me.

'It's easier said than done, Ella. How can I get a job without registration?'

'Well, we'll think of something. The simplest way is for you to get married.'

'You mean to pay somebody for a fake marriage?'

'Why not? You are pretty, clever, stylish! What else do men want?'

'Thank you very much. You've made my day. But no, I don't think it's that easy.'

'Say no more. You don't need to think at all. I'll do all the thinking.' Considering that Ella, only five years older than me, was single made the whole conversation even funnier.

I need to explain what "registration" meant and why it was it so important to have it if you wanted to work in Moscow. All Soviet citizens from the age of sixteen had to have an internal passport. It contained all the usual information: your name, date and place of birth, your nationality and the registration, the rubber stamp with your address which had to be obtained from the local militia office. If you moved from one place in the country to another you had to inform the militia officials and get a new stamp at the new place. Some cities had restrictions on registration. They simply would not register a newcomer if he did not have any close family already registered there. From that point of view Moscow was the worst of all. In Soviet times, living in Moscow was a privilege. The capital was better supplied than the rest of the hungry country. That privilege could be traded. The Moscow authorities used it to attract new workers if the city was short of builders or cleaners, for instance. Individuals tried to do the same. Stories of bachelors making cash through arranged marriages, or of some young provincial sex bomb using an innocent Muscovite in order to get registration, became part of local folklore.

That is why, when the trouble in Chechnya started, I had never spent any time speculating on moving to Moscow. Orel suited me very well, I was happy with the way things were going there. I gave a presentation to the local administration, describing our ideas for bringing foreign investors to Orel. They agreed to give it a try and suggested one of the mechanical plants for the purpose. It looked as if my scary business trips were proving worthwhile.

Back at home, life became more and more dangerous. Every time I returned to Grozny, I was on the phone to all my friends, desperate to know how they were. One bright sunny morning, I was waiting for Vera, who had promised to drop in. We didn't even dream of going out any more, but at least in the safety of our own four walls we could still enjoy each other's company and have some good times. I was baking biscuits. The smell of vanilla mingled with the fragrance of lilac from the open window. I had a table laid out on our long terrace-type balcony. We could have a meal and a good girly talk and enjoy the view: the gardens full of lilac blossom and the red tiled roofs freshly washed by overnight rain. The doorbell rang. Opening the door, first of all I saw a massive bunch of lilac, a whole bush. Vera's face was hidden behind it.

'This is from my mother's garden,' she said.

When I took the flowers from her, I noticed her eyes were red. I could see she was trying to do her best with a cheerful voice and smile, but she was definitely upset.

'What's the matter, Verochka? Please don't pretend

with me. Take your coat off and sit down and tell me what has happened.'

Then I saw that the right side of her elegant white coat was covered with stripes of mud.

'Is that why you are upset? Did you slip on the pavement?'

'No, I didn't. I was standing at the bus stop, waiting for a bus. I was looking forward to seeing you and fully determined to enjoy myself for the next couple of hours. You know, the sun was shining, for once I felt happy, probably it was written all over my face. One of those young Chechens, who are supporting the new regime these days, was passing by. He saw me standing there. I don't know, probably something in the way I looked annoyed him. He came up to me, lifted his foot and smeared the mud off his dirty boot on my coat.'

'Bastard! Were there no other people with you at the bus stop?'

'Oh, plenty! Nobody said a word. He was carrying a gun.' Vera was crying now. 'I know it's not a big deal, but, oh, Sonechka darling, it's so humiliating! Why did he do it?'

'Never mind, dear, there is nothing we can do about it. Let's just forget it. Do you want to stay with us tonight?'

'No. No, thank you. My mother would be worried. I'll be all right. I am now. Honestly. Tell me about Moscow. Where have you been? What have you seen?'

But never mind the exciting news from Moscow, the news at home was shocking. The first Chechen president had been elected. The election had not been as peaceful as the new government wanted it to appear. Some former members of the government had been assassinated, others had been forced out of the republic. A squadron of Russian troops, normally present in every big city of Russia, had been moved out of Chechnya, leaving the arsenals behind practically unguarded. Why? Maybe it was part of some crooked plan? Within a week these arsenals had been taken over by the president's men. Had they simply been sold to the new administration by the corrupt generals? Nobody could prove it, but that was what the local people were thinking.

In the past, Russians were naïve enough to think that the Russian government would not let them be killed one after another. Now we knew we had been let down. I do believe that the new Chechen president did not intentionally plan to terrorise the Russian population. He had given freedom to his people and everything depended on how they used that freedom. Unfortunately for us, many of them believed it was a licence for violence. Is there something in human nature that brings the worst to the surface as soon as people are left unsupervised? For me it was the time when I became aware that the only real "law" is the law inside you. Your own good or bad will.

One morning I met Alikhan in town. His first question was 'How can I help you in these hard times?' He looked cheerful and was immaculately dressed as usual. He told me that he had taken a post in the new government as a Foreign Affairs adviser. He invited me into his office in the old Communist Party Commitee building. The entrance was guarded by two young men armed with Kalashnikovs. We talked for a while about old times in the Cooperative Union, about our families, the usual conversation of people who had once worked together and then hadn't met for a while. I decided to ask if he could help us to clear Alexei of the stupid accusation of being a "Russian spy".

136

'Do you remember, Alikhan, that you advised me to run away from Grozny, when I was leaving the Union for the Korean Joint Venture? Now there is a real opportunity for me to move, but there's a problem. I wonder if you could help me?'

I told him about the situation with our company. He promised his assistance.

'Can you explain to me what's going on, Alikhan? Is this the life the new government wanted for its people? Why did it go so wrong? We are all sitting in our houses hiding like mice.'

'I know, Sofia. I am so sorry it has come to this. Believe me, the Chechens are as scared as you Russians. You see, now that we have our independence, we need to defend it. We need a good army and where can we get it if not from conscription of the youth? At the present time they are just young men from the mountains. They need discipline and skills. That will come later. Now they probably don't know the difference between high spirits and a hooligan outburst. It will all sort itself out. We know from history that every revolution has its victims.'

'Well, I see. So you think, given time, the streets will be safe again?'

'Absolutely!'

I left Alikhan's office if not reassured, then somewhat relieved. We do choose what to believe, don't we?

It was still early afternoon when I was on my way back home. I knew Alexandra and Lisa must be back from school. Alexandra's timetable had been changed, she never stayed late now. She opened the door for me. When I looked up at her, I felt my heart stop. Her face and bare arms were badly bruised, she was pressing her hand to her right side.

'What's happened? For God's sake, what has happened to you?'

'Mama, don't worry, they didn't rape me. I'll be okay. You'll see, I'll be fine, it's only bruises, nothing's broken.' She tried to calm me down, my brave little girl. Nelly jumped on to her lap as soon as she sat down.

'I finished school early today. The maths teacher was sick. I decided to go and see granny Polya.'

Granny Polya, my ex-mother-in-law, lived two streets down from the school on the opposite side of the town from our house. She had cancer, and had been bed-ridden for some time by then.

'I was only there for half an hour. Granddad offered to see me back, but I said I would be all right. It was only two o'clock. On my way back I was stopped by two Chechen lads. The street was empty. They started dragging me into the nearest house with them. I ran away from them, they caught me and then hit me, but I didn't go with them anyway. They said "You know our law, you little Russian bitch, if you want to live here, you have to do what the older people say, especially if they are men". I said I was not local, I had come from Russia to see my grandmother. Then they let me go. It's all over now, mum. I'm fine.'

I cried that night with anger, anger at my own weakness and inability to protect my child. Alexandra recovered physically, but not mentally. She could not make herself leave the flat after what had happened. On my next trip to Moscow I took her and Lisa with me and left them in Ella's care. She is much better now, but even here, in Moscow, when she sees someone who looks like a Chechen, I can feel her hand trembling in mine.

The project in Orel was in full swing and I was sure we could move there very soon. The negotiations between one of the South Korean companies and the plant resulted in a draft contract. According to this, the first stage of delivery of the parts had to be covered by a thirty percent down payment. It was not a bad outcome at all, considering the insecurity of time and place. It was all that the plant could afford. When I arrived in Moscow a day before the agreed date of signing the contract, I was flabbergasted by the news of the tremendous collapse of the rouble. When the director of the plant rang me I knew what he was going to say. They could not pay the agreed amount. The project was put on hold. But I could not leave my life in such a state of uncertainty. The company was still moving to Orel, but the chances of starting business in the near future were very slim.

During my stays in Moscow, I sometimes did interpreting for some of my old clients from the Grozny Cooperative Union. The extra cash was always useful. On one of these occasions, I met Makhmud, a young Chechen businessman. He was introduced by someone I knew very well with the comment that we could be useful to each other. Makhmud was very straightforward.

'Sofia, you have been recommended to me by so many people, I hope we shall come to some sort of business agreement. I have some money, enough to organise a small business. I'd like to set up a joint venture with a foreign partner.'

'All right, I'll think what I can do for you.' I said, actually thinking 'God bless you, mate, you popped up on time with your money.'

The Moscow Project

That night, at Ella's apartment, all four of us were thinking of how to deal with the two things: our move to Moscow and the feasibility of Makhmud's business plans. Ella was sitting at the kitchen table, with rollers in her hair, wearing a black, Japanese-style housecoat. A multicoloured embroidered dragon adorned her back. Alexandra, Lisa and I were also in our dressing gowns and wearing woolly socks borrowed from our hostess. We were southern girls and it took time to get used to Moscow temperatures.

'Look, Sofia, this could be an opportunity for you to get settled in Moscow. If we register his company here, you could do some kind of executive work in it.'

'Yes, in that case I wouldn't need Moscow registration, because it would be a private company. But am I right in thinking that to register a company in Moscow one has to be a Muscovite?'

'Yes, and that's where I can help you. We can put it in my name.'

'Brilliant! Thank you Ella.'

What was the next step? On one of my trips to the trade exhibitions, I had met a business lady from the Hungarian Chamber of Commerce and we had kept in touch. I heard from her that the part of Hungarian industry that had been oriented towards the Socialist bloc market in the past was now in a shambles, furniture producers, for instance, especially the small factories. I hardly slept that night but by the morning my offer was ready. I phoned Makhmud and invited him to see us at Ella's apartment.

He came with a bottle of wine, chocolates and flowers, a gentleman from the Caucasus. We had some snacks ready, but agreed that business must come first. I presented my Hungarian furniture factory project. I had drawn up a scheme showing how we could build up his business, giving him a rough idea of costs and timing. He accepted it right away. We agreed that he would employ Ella and me to deal with registration of his company. Ella promised to find an accountant.

He asked me to give him a price for the whole deal and it was then that I revealed to him that there was a catch. This was also the fruit of my sleepless night. Of course, having permanent work was an important issue for me, but the most important issue was my family's safety so I had provided my project with a parallel strategy.

Phase One: Ella and I would start legal procedures for the company registration in Moscow. At the same time, in Grozny, Makhmud would organise a truck to move my belongings to Moscow. When the registration was through he would buy my flat in Grozny. I would rent a flat in Moscow, then bring granny Asya, and all four of us would move into it as soon as our furniture and belongings arrived. Only at that point would I hand the registration documents over to Makhmud.

Phase Two: Makhmud would employ Ella and me to run his company, a full time job for me and a part-time one for Ella. I would introduce him at the Hungarian Chamber of Commerce. My friend at the Chamber would help us to find a partner in Hungary. After visiting the country and choosing a factory we would be ready to sign the papers for a joint venture.

Without going into the logistics and marketing details, Phase Three was to run the business together for two years or until we both decided we were ready to move on. For myself, I decided I would stay until I had made enough money to buy myself a flat in Moscow and have us all registered there. Then I would get on with my professional career.

Unfortunately, as usual, reality produced a much tougher variant. Phase One proceeded smoothly without any deviation from the plan. The money I received for my flat in Grozny, sold at a crisis price, was by no means sufficient to buy me anything in Moscow but it covered six months' rent for a tiny one-room-and-a-kitchen flat in Davydkovo. My Moscow landlady happened to be an accountant so we decided to look no further and offered her a job.

I made my last trip to Grozny to pack and prepare my granny Asya, Nelly the dog and Yashka the parrot for the trip to Moscow. We could only go by train. The night before our departure, I left grandma with the luggage, and Yashka in his cage at Lena's. Lena was allergic to dogs so I returned to the empty flat to stay overnight with Nelly. I was glad I did, I was desperate for a break. Trying to make leaving easier for grandma, I was painting in all colours of the rainbow pictures of our future happiness in Moscow. She in her turn was pretending to believe in it to keep me happy. After having been so extremely busy with hundreds of things to be done, this double play exhausted us both. With a little time to myself, I knew I had a last chance to let out my emotions. I was walking through the bare rooms of my flat, so cosy not long ago, with Nelly following me, wagging her tail and showing unconditional trust.

'I wish I were as sure in myself as you are in me, Nelly.' I wanted to have a good cry but my eyes were dry and hot. As hot as the sudden thrust of pain somewhere between the ribs in the middle of my chest that made me bend double.

'Damn! This is the last thing we need now, isn't it, Nelly? Let's see if we have anything left in the medical cabinet.' The cabinet in the bathroom was empty. The phone was cut off. On the kitchen windowsill there was a bottle of vodka. I had bought a dozen bottles for the men hired to load the truck. That one had somehow been left behind. It had been opened but was nearly full. It was not my usual kind of drink but I hardly had a choice. I found a cup, filled it and made myself drink it all. The drink gave me the numbness I was looking for. I filled my cup once again, and then again till the bottle was empty and I was so drunk I could cry. I was whining out loud, sitting on the filthy kitchen floor feeling sorry for myself, a luxury I knew I could afford probably for the last time in my life.

I woke up at dawn feeling terribly sick and spent the next four hours vomiting my guts out. I have never drunk vodka since. Having spent the morning embracing the loo, I arrived at Lena's carrying Nelly in a basket and feeling transparently clean. I found grandma terribly upset. That morning she had fed Yashka and probably left his cage door open. When Lena opened the window later on, off he flew straight through the window on to the branch of a plum tree outside. They had tried to catch him, even borrowed a net from the boy next door, but the air of freedom had made him reckless and he had flown away. Poor, stupid bird.

'Oh, I am so sorry. It was my fault. What shall I tell the girls?' Grandma was crying. And I knew she was crying not only over the parrot. She was crying over everything she had to leave behind: the graves of the loved ones, the town full of memories, a shrinking circle of old friends.

'It's not your fault at all. The girls will understand. Please, grandma, come down. You have always said our

Lord gives us only as much as we can deal with. Isn't this just another trial for us? I need you to be strong and help me with the girls. Who else can I rely on in bringing them up? Think of them meeting us at the Kazanskyi railway station in Moscow in just two days' time.'

In Moscow

I wanted my little team to accept our move with the feeling of a happy ending. In spite of being cramped in a tiny flat, we lived now in the capital of the country, a dream city for many people, and I wanted the girls to start taking advantage of it straightaway. I was very busy with my new project but at least once a week we took a stroll in the centre to Red Square, visiting the Kremlin museums or doing something else touristy. We even took granny to a pop singer's concert, a Russian crooner, whom she had never dreamt of hearing live. Soon there was the possibility of enjoying the picturesque Russian countryside as well.

Pursuing her matrimonial plans on my behalf, Ella invited me to one of the private fine art exhibitions. The landscapes I saw there were tranquil, even surreal, from where I was standing in the reality of my own life. Walking from one landscape to another among a crowd of people who seemed to know each other very well, I did not see Ella coming up with an average-looking middle aged man.

'Sofia, meet my friend Afanasey Volodin, the creator of this beauty.'

We shook hands and I complimented him on his work. He thanked me and was swept away by another wave of visitors. Ella, who had disappeared somewhere, returned with two glasses of champagne.

'So what do you think? Do you like him?' she asked.

'Yes, I was genuine when I said I liked his pictures.'

'You'll drive me crazy, girl. Do you like him as a man?'

'No, why should I?'

'Because he is a widower, and a Muscovite and, as you see, an established artist. A perfect candidate.'

'Ella, I seriously think you should stop campaigning…'

'And I think you should stop being so bloody serious! Give yourself a chance. Have a drink. Give us a smile. There are plenty of interesting men around. Look, he's coming back.'

'Sorry, we were rudely interrupted. Ella mentioned you were from Northern Caucasus. I was born in Vladikavkaz myself. My parents moved to Moscow when I was a child. How long have you lived in Moscow?'

'About a month,' I said, 'I'm from Grozny'.

His expression changed. Instead of general social politeness there was kindness and empathy now.

'Oh, you did the right thing leaving the place. I can only imagine how dangerous it was there.'

'Yes, it still is, Afanasey.'

'Do you have a family? Are they with you?'

'Yes, my two daughters and my grandmother.'

Somebody else was seeking his attention. He apologised and, before passing to some other people, handed me his card.

'Please Sofia, promise to call me tomorrow morning. We must see each other soon.'

I did not phone him. Why should I? And I was very surprised when he rang me.

'Hello Sofia. This is Afanasey Volodin. We met yesterday at my exhibition. You haven't called me. I persuaded Ella to give me your number, I hope you don't mind.'

'Not at all, Afanasey. How are you?'

'Couldn't be better. I wonder if you would like to bring your daughters to see me at my studio. Most of my friends' children are ecstatic when they come to see me. My cave is full of wild animals. Well not too wild, don't worry, cats and dogs. Shall I give you my address?'

'Thank you, Afanasey, I'll have to ask the girls.'

'Then ask them now, I'll wait.' He was persistent.

It was Sunday and it was raining. We had no special plans. The girls were pleased with the idea of seeing an artist's studio and were ready in no time. After a short but enthusiastic discussion, we decided to take a basket with half a homemade beef pie and some aubergine pesto: a little of the flavour of our host's native Vladikavkaz.

Pressing the bell on the door of the ground floor studio in a shabby but stylish constructivist building overlooking the Moskva river, we agreed that the house stank of cats. When the door opened we could see why. Letting us in, Afanasey greeted us heartily:

'Come on in, girls, over here. Meet my lodgers. Don't worry if you step on them, it's their problem, the lazy rascals.'

Cats were everywhere, on every level of his spacious cave. It was obvious why he called it a cave: behind the folds of colourful Russian scarves, faded velvet and silk, Persian carpets, icons, pictures and antique clutter powdered with dust, you could still see the walls tiled with stone, a dream design of the seventies. The only clean surface was a big shining window overlooking the river.

'Push the cats away and take a seat, young ladies. What can I get you? Tea, coffee, hot chocolate? Have a look in that corner over there, Sofia, there are some pictures from the series you saw at the exhibition. Didn't have enough space for them.'

Afanasey insisted on serving the drinks. Shocked by

the lack of hygiene in his studio, I offered to help him. It was a big relief for me to find that his small kitchen was forbidden territory for the cats. He even kept it locked, explaining that otherwise his fluffy lodgers would occupy it by storm as soon as no one was watching. I could see that some of them had been laying siege already.

'You bandits, go away. Daddy has already fed you. Come here, Lucky, give Daddy a kiss. Have I scared you, baby? No, no, Daddy is not angry with you. Excuse me, pet, you're staying here. Now you've met my family too, Sofia.'

Watching Afanasey with his cats, I could see the whole spectrum of emotions he had been going through: he was embarrassed, annoyed with them for his embarrassment, ashamed of his anger which he felt was a sort of betrayal. After all, they were his family.

'We love pets, Afanasey.' I thought he needed a bit of support. It was nice of him to invite us to his sacred place. 'I had a cat called Pusska when I was small. She was a very close friend of mine. Quite a character too. How many cats do you have altogether?'

'Well, twenty. Maybe twenty two. They bring them all the time. Leave them on my door step. What can I do?'

'Who are "they"?'

'The neighbours. Everyone in the neighbourhood knows I pick them up.'

'Have you always had cats?'

'When my wife was alive there were only two. She died two years ago of cancer. Since then the cats have occupied this studio one way or another. They keep me company.'

While talking I was washing the cups, which didn't look clean enough for me. The basket we had brought was a nice surprise for the artist.

'Oh, my God, it smells like childhood. Only my mother could cook aubergines like this. In Moscow they don't even know what to do with the vegetable. Thank you, Sofia.'

'You're welcome. My grandmother made it. The girls helped her. I don't have time for cooking, Afanasey.'

The drinks were ready. Afanasey took the tray with cups, biscuits and chocolates. The kitchen door was locked again. Back in the studio we found an idyllic scene. Lisa was lying flat on the sofa, covered with cats, from head to toe.

'Look mama, I am seven cats tall!'

Alexandra had a white puppy on her lap. 'Is this the only dog you have?'

'There are actually two more, but I locked them in the broom cupboard before you came. They fight with the cats. I didn't want to scare you.'

Alexandra and Lisa insisted on letting the prisoners out. They started fighting with a big ginger cat, or was the cat the initiator? Never mind. The girls were reasoning that both parties were to blame. I heard them really laughing. I was so happy to see them relaxed. The party was definitely a success. When we were leaving, Afanasey invited us all to join him the following weekend on his trip to the country. He said he painted outdoors all year round, knew the Moscow countryside like his own backyard.

That was how we spent our first summer in Moscow. Our only regret was that granny didn't want to join us on these trips. She did not like the underground. Unfortunately on our trips to the countryside we used only public transport. Afanasey told us that since surviving a car accident many years ago he had avoided using a car, even as a passenger. But granny said she was glad to have some time to herself.

We did not have much privacy, with all four of us sharing one room. We were tremendously inventive with our sleeping accommodation. The girls and granny slept in the room where there were two sofas and a long chair-bed. I arranged a folding camp bed for myself in the kitchen. It was far from comfortable but gave me some privacy. The kitchen also served as my office.

Our business arrangements were moving steadily on to the next stage, but with some bureaucratic delays. The date of our trip to Budapest had been arranged for September. In the meantime Mahkmud became a frequent guest at Ella's flat. There was more than one reason. Ella had suggested we might use her flat as a company office for now. We equipped it with a computer and a fax machine. Our daily activities did not require Makhmud's constant presence, but it was clear that he was very much impressed with our energetic and bubbly office manager. She obviously enjoyed his attention and let him accompany her to film premieres and other social events. After all, he was a handsome young man, maybe too young to be taken seriously, but seriousness in affairs of the heart had never been a virtue in Ella's bohemian circle.

Once, she phoned me in the early hours, saying that she had just taken Makhmud to the emergency hospital. He had been complaining of stomach ache for a while, and it turned out to be an inflamed appendix. She had had to call for an ambulance and now Makhmud was on his way to the operating theatre. That was how I knew that they had become lovers. Ella said she had been reluctant to tell me because we both knew he had a family back in Grozny, but who was I to judge my cousin. I had always loved her, and after all her support she was simply beyond any criticism. I hoped she wouldn't be hurt in this relationship, that was

150

all I cared about. Makhmud's operation was successful. Ella insisted he moved to her place for some time after it. Our trip to Budapest was postponed indefinitely. When Makhmud suggested we might do a bit of trading and send a truckload of sweets and biscuits to Grozny, I found a good deal with a confectionery factory. It gave us a nice profit.

Makhmud went to Grozny for a while and came back with a suggestion. He said he was going to apply for bank credit. I was surprised but not in the least disappointed. I knew our company had enough capital to start the business. And it had been his business after all. He said he knew an accountancy firm who would help us with the paperwork. Then he told us he had to go back to Grozny again for a little while. Not more then a week, he said. But after a week had passed, another young man arrived on our doorstep with a pack containing the papers required for the bank credit. He introduced himself as Makhmud's younger brother.

'Makhmud sent me to you with these papers. Everything is ready, you have only to put your signatures here and here, and the money will be transferred to your company account.'

'Very good, thank you for delivering the papers,' I said, 'And where is Makhmud?'

'He is still in Grozny. Family business.'

'So when is he actually planning to come back?'

'Oh, very soon. In about two or three days.'

'I see. Let me have a look at the papers again. You see, considering it was his idea, I'm sure Makhmud would like to sign them himself.'

And with these words I locked the papers in the desk. The young man left without even finishing his coffee. And we started waiting for Makhmud. He did not come back, not in a week, not in a month. We never saw him again. There was no reply from his contact phones in Grozny. To complete the picture, the bank statement we received at the end of the month showed no money in the account. All Makhmud's friends we had known in Moscow had also disappeared. We didn't know what to think. Or rather, we were afraid to voice our worst fears.

So there I was, with no money to live on and no job. In addition to responsibility for my family, I was left on my own to run a company I did not need. A quarterly balance was due and I had to pay an accountant to deal with it. The only solution I could think of was to find some kind of interpreting or translation job. I renewed my South Korean connections and was in luck there. They needed weekend tour guides to take their visitors round Moscow. In her professional capacity, Ella came across a film dubbing company and recommended me to them.

When the first heat had subsided, I was able to think more clearly of what to do about our company. I decided to consult the solicitors and made an appointment to meet the same young lawyers who had helped us to register the company. They looked very young, probably recent graduates. Namesakes, both called Igor, they addressed each other by their family names, Petrov and Senkin, for convenience and because they thought it was cool. When I told them what had happened to the company and to me, they offered their help to sell it. They were not very surprised at Makhmud's trick. Since the economy and finance of the country were no longer under state control, corruption had rocketed to the sky. As they explained to me, one of the latest scams was to find a corrupt banker who would arrange a loan for a company. When the loan was received it would be divided between the owner of the company and the banker. After that the owner would declare himself bankrupt or just disappear as had happened in my case. What about the banker? Well, that depended on his preference. He might be somewhere in Cyprus, for instance, or possibly he had sent his money there first. How could he be checked? And who would care to check him?

Both Petrov and Senkin were impressed with my cleverness when I told them how I had refused to sign the loan papers. I did not want to disillusion them, but I hadn't really known at the time why I had locked away those papers. Thank God I had. I could only imagine what would have happened to me when the banker disappeared to Cyprus and Makhmud to Chechnya!

But the main outcome of our conversation was that Petrov and Senkin offered me a job in their company.

'Now I can tell you, Sofia, you were our first client,' said Petrov. 'Since then we've been registering two or three companies a month. We are thinking of expanding our services and taking foreign clients too. If you don't mind carrying papers between offices, answering phone calls and serving coffee to the clients when you are not busy with your paper work, maybe you would like to join us?'

'But if it were a foreign client, then I would conduct the consultation, you would do the interpreting and Petrov would serve us coffee.'

'Or vice versa. I mean Senkin is more experienced with trays. He had a job as a waiter in the summer vacation. And I'm good at building cowsheds.'

'I like your offer. Thank you. But I must tell you, I don't have Moscow registration.'

'It's okay. This is a private firm. Now let's discuss your wages.'

Unfortunately, they could not pay me enough to keep me going. I explained to Petrov and Senkin that to pay my way I needed to keep working both as a tour guide and with the film translation. They didn't mind. They even offered me the use of the company office and computer after office hours. That was how I ended up here in the centre of Moscow not far from *Patriarshii Prudy*, in this old building that once had been the home of a large family from the Moscow gentry, now sliced up and shared like a birthday cake.

After five in the evening, when the building is empty and dark, it regains its past glamour. This very room might have been someone's bedroom. A tiled heating stove stands in the corner, tall windows overlook the garden. My imagination dresses them with pale cream curtains. I lay the sophisticated luxury of a Turkish carpet on the floor. What next? A bed and a dressing table. Now I can see that it's a girl's bedroom. She is a young debutante and heiress of the family, like Natasha Rostova. I could tell her story, but there is work to be done. I need to finish the Scooby-Doo script for dubbing.

When she typed the last Scooby-Dooby-Doo, it was a quarter to eleven. She rang home and told granny that she was on her way. She knew the old lady would be waiting for her. After Grozny the streets of Moscow seemed safe. The fear that had haunted her since the night of the riot in Grozny had gone. The girls were safe and well. She had made it. Deep in her heart she was proud of herself. That was the feeling that gave her confidence and strength for another battle, this time a financial one.

It was raining. Navigating her umbrella in the gusts of cold October wind along the crooked lanes, she was thinking that Christmas was not far away. She wanted it to be normal, with presents and a tree and delicious food, now available in all varieties on the shelves of Moscow shops. With the declining number of tourists, to fulfil her Christmas plans she needed another job. It was midnight when she opened the door of the flat. The girls were in bed. Granny put the kettle on.

'There are some *bliny* in the oven for you, Sonechka. And Afanasey has been entertaining me on the phone again. He asked you to give him a call no matter how late it was.'

'Thank you, granny, I will.'

Their weekend trips to the country had had to be stopped when she lost her job with Makhmud's company. She had to spend all her weekends accompanying tourists. She took the girls to Afanasey's studio from time to time. Sometimes he invited Sofia out to his friends' houses or to exhibitions. But whatever kind of friendship it was, there was definitely nothing romantic from her side. He was a kind man, an interesting personality. Sometimes she had found it rather flattering that he introduced her to his friends. Sofia was happy to leave it this way, but she had a feeling they were both coming to the point where that important question would have to be asked, one way or another. She was in no doubt as far as his amorous intentions were concerned. That was why she was now dreading dialling his number. She knew the answer, her heart never flickered once when he casually put his arm round her shoulders or gave her a peck on the cheek. Dreading it or not, she had to ring him and she did. He was waiting for her call and asked if she could go with him to a big society party the following week. He said the restaurant where it was going to take place was within walking distance of his flat. The party was expected to go on till the early hours. He suggested Sofia might stay with him afterwards.

'Please say you will, Sofia, dear. And as for your sleeping in my bed, I won't deny I've been dreaming about it for a while now, but I assure you I'm not a rapist.'

Sofia was laughing: 'Aha, that's what all you men say to us poor innocent creatures.'

'Poor creature! I've lost so much weight, my clothes are dropping off since I met you, my mermaid.'

Never mind her feelings, or the absence of them, he was fun. Sofia felt it would be stupid to turn down his invitation. Nevertheless, later on, lying in a hot bath before going to bed, the only luxury she could still afford, she was fantasizing about Mark inviting her to go out with him and asking her to stay at his place afterwards. Oh, there would not be any doubt about her answer in that case.

Mark. Back to Life

'Sofiya, Sofiya,' a high pitched voice was calling from somewhere,
'Sofiya, ven aquí. ¿Donde estás? Sofiya!' Suddenly the sound of this distant voice broke the silence around him: soft laughter, other voices talking, quick steps passing, the clink of a glass. Then there was the light. Was he asleep? Someone's white sleeve emerged from the milky fog that surrounded him. He could see a hand adjusting something on a stand in front of him. Some kind of medication? He was in hospital. Why? What had happened to him? He began to drift effortlessly back into his milky fog. Then he remembered the first sound that had woken him. "Sofiya" replayed somewhere deep in his conscious. A fresh wave of memory brought him back. He remembered it all now. How long had he been here?

'Sofia,' he said, 'I need to call Sofia.' His mouth was dry and his stiff lips refused to articulate the words.

'Good Heavens! He's awake! Hello, Mark.' His name, pronounced with a strong "r", sounded strange to him.

He saw a pair of brown eyes, the kind cheerful face of an elderly nurse.

'You'll be fine, Mark. You'll be just fine.'

On the plane from Karaganda to Moscow and then on to Malaga he was busy planning the coming week. If he stayed focused he could be back in Grozny in four, or at the most five days. The past week in Karaganda was like the blurred picture you got if you moved your camera too quickly. He was embarrassed to see Katya waiting for him at the airport. He had totally forgotten about her. She was intending to follow him to his flat, but he said he was tired

157

and asked Sergey to give her a lift back home. Everyone already knew they were closing. Next day he invited all his staff to a restaurant for a farewell party.

'So I guess you are not taking me back to Spain with you, Mark?' asked Katya, taking a seat next to him when the band started playing and most of their colleagues had left the table.

'No, Katya, I'm sorry. I'm sure you'll meet someone younger to make your dreams come true.'

'Sure I will.' She pushed her chair back and headed to the dance floor. Occasionally he saw her angry eyes staring at him but she never spoke to him again.

Spring in Spain was the way spring in Spain should be: beautiful, full of fragrances and expectation. On his way from Malaga airport to Fuengirola Mark imagined how he would show Sofia his wonderland: trees in full bloom under the bluest sky one could imagine. And how all the shades of blue blended in the sea, bringing up white yachts from the horizon. She would be with him to watch the sun setting and, best of all, she would be there for the sunrise too.

The next day started with a meeting at the developer's office. He was very pleased with the job they had done. Mark's cheque was even better then he had expected.

'It includes your bonus, too, Mark. You did a very good job. What are your plans now? Going back home to the UK?'

'I have some unfinished business in Russia. I'm planning to go back shortly.'

'I wouldn't do that if I were you. Well, Russia is big – as long as you're not anywhere near Karaganda, you'll be all right.'

'Pardon? What's wrong with Karaganda? It's not that

158

I'm going there, but anyway?'

'You might come across some angry clients there, you know.'

No, Mark did not know, but he was beginning to understand. They had made a fool of him. The whole business had been one big scam, and he had been at the centre of it.

'You bloody bastards! People trusted me. They treated me like a friend. What must they be thinking of me? You must do something about it. Find a resort and accommodate them there. Any resort. Not necessarily top quality. Just anything!'

'What's your problem, Mark? Don't you like your cheque? Let's go to the restaurant at the marina tonight. Have a nice time and forget about it. All right?'

'Listen, if you're not going to do anything about it, I have all the records of the people who bought from us. I will write to them, I promise you, I will'

'Don't do anything silly, Mark. Okay, okay, if you insist, I'll think of something. Probably you are right. See you later tonight. We'll talk about it.'

On the way back to his rented flat in Benalmadena, Mark stopped for a nice talk with Sofia on the phone, told her that there was a small issue to resolve and then his business here would be finished for now. He promised that next time he called it would be with details of his flight to Moscow. Then he paid a visit to his landlord, asking him if it was possible to install a landline telephone in his apartment and the landlord promised to sort it out.

That night Mark met Martin in one of the bars of the marina, between Benalmadena and Torremolinos. He was accompanied by two well built young men whom Mark had never seen before. Martin introduced them as his friends. They had a couple of drinks in the bar, then a dinner in the restaurant with wine, then brandy. It was well after midnight when they were ready to leave. Martin's friends said they lived in Mark's neighbourhood. They shared a taxi.

In the morning Mark was found lying in a pool of blood by a next-door neighbour. She called for the police and an ambulance. He was unconscious but alive. The doctors said he had been badly beaten and struck on his head from behind with some heavy object. He spent two months in a coma. As soon as he was able to talk, he gave the police officer a description of the men who had shared the taxi with him. But they could find neither them, nor Martin nor Jack. Even the office where Martin had held his meeting with them was rented out to another company. But the biggest regret for Mark was that since he had been able to talk again he had not been able to get in touch with Sofia. There was no reply from her telephones. He was desperate to go back to Russia. But it took another month for him to learn to walk again.

Sofia's Big Night Out in Moscow

Sofia was happy. She did not turn down the invitation. All four of them took part in the preparations. She couldn't remember where her special occasion gowns were so the girls fetched all the suitcases from the cupboard. When they were found, Lisa wanted first to try them all herself. After serious debate, three gowns, black, purple and green, were chosen. They were a size too big for her now. The black one was turned down: 'Mama, you look like a Mafia widow from an Italian film in it.' Alexandra had always been pretty straightforward. Sofia put away the purple one herself: 'Too low cut, and besides, I would need a new bra for it. No, definitely not.' The green gown was made of silk jersey with long tight lace sleeves. It was that deep ashy shade of green, which gave her eyes a bright slightly vampish look. Lisa found some silver earrings and a matching necklace in her mother's jewellery box. Sofia thought the earrings were interesting enough by themselves, but she decided against the necklace, it would have been too much.

She let herself to get involved in a whole makeover and added dark red lipstick to her make-up. When colouring her hair next time she substituted her natural light brown with a copper brown. Her hair was long enough to put up in a simple but stylish hairdo. On the night of the party she felt very much like Cinderella on her way to the ball, fully aware of her radiant beauty. After unanimous approval from the girls, her most severe critics, and with Granny's blessing, Sofia walked to the bus stop. She was wearing high heels, not the best footwear for public transport, especially the escalators in the underground, but she couldn't afford a taxi.

'Hello, fairy,' she was greeted on the bus by a rough old man, who had obviously had too much to drink.

'So do fairies come down to the big cities nowadays? I beg your pardon, miss, I didn't mean to trouble you, it's nice to see a pretty, cheerful face. Looks like you don't know anything about the problems people have, sweetheart, do you?'

'As a matter of fact, I do.'

'Oh, what is it you need right now, sugar plum?'

'A pumpkin.'

'A pumpkin? Why?'

'To make into a carriage.'

Afanasey met her on the platform of the Metro station. Sofia noticed that his evening jacket made him look like a waiter. He was lucky he did not have to wear formal outfits very often. He looked younger in his everyday casual clothes. He handed her a big bunch of white roses, a gesture she considered a bit out of place.

'Sofia, you will be queen of the ball tonight.'

And she was. Afanasey, mingling with the crowd, shaking hands with men, kissing and complimenting women, never let her drift too far away.

'Oh, what the hell,' Sofia was thinking, 'I might as well enjoy myself for once in my life.'

The next day she could hardly remember what she had been talking about, but the names of the famous actors, film-makers, writers and artists she kept mentioning made the girls at home scream. She was drinking a lot, too. Champagne, cocktails, some of them she was trying for the first time in her life. A jazz band was playing. The first couples appeared on the dance floor. She was dancing too, mostly with Afanasey. She was surprised by his firm but caring grip and his good sense of rhythm. It had been two in the morning when the party started to break up. Faces began to perspire, postures were not too steady. Afanasey suggested they went home. Sofia's feet were aching.

'I wish we could call for a taxi, Afanasey. My feet are absolutely on fire.'

'I would prefer to carry you in my arms, my dear. But okay, maybe I won't freak out this time. It's only five minutes' drive from here.'

When in the taxi Sofia cursed her selfishness, watching Afanasey, panic-stricken and pale faced. Thank God it really was only for five minutes.

Although she was a frequent visitor to Afanasey's studio, Sofia had never been invited upstairs to his flat. She did not expect anything different from his derelict studio and was speechless when he opened the door and let her in. Everything was freshly decorated and brand new.

'Do come in and make yourself at home. You will find a vase for your flowers over there on the shelf. I think I need a drink. Would you like one?' He was still shaking after the taxi ride. At the restaurant he had asked the waitress to look after the roses he had given her, now she had brought them here. She took her shoes off, found a crystal vase for the flowers and stretched out on the sofa.

'It's a nice apartment. Have you just finished decorating?'

'Yes, you are absolutely right, my darling. It was finished this week. You see, after my wife died two years ago, I simply locked it up and moved down to the studio. The truth is I had an invitation to this party well in advance. I wanted you to come too and thought you might stay with me. But you know the way I live in my studio. Invite you there? I'm not that daft. I'm having a cognac, Sonechka.

Would you like one too?'

'Yes, please.' She was suddenly tired. The light-hearted atmosphere of the party had disappeared. He came up with the glasses, sat next to her. Feeling uneasy, she downed her cognac in a gulp. He took away her glass.

'How are your feet? Still hurting?' He started massaging her toes. There was a warm relaxing sensation from his fingers. Sofia closed her eyes and …. immediately fell asleep.

Next morning she woke up lying on the same sofa under a fluffy blanket still wearing her green dress. It was nearly eleven o'clock. Feeling terrible, and disgusted with her smudged make-up, she went straight to the bathroom and had a long hot shower. She found herself a dressing gown and as she combed her hair she wondered where her host was. It was very quiet in the flat. Well, he wasn't in. She was alone, she realised with relief. On the kitchen table there was a note. 'Hi, I am downstairs feeding the cats. Be back soon.' Sofia made herself a cup of strong black coffee. He was giving her time to choose what to do in this situation. Wasn't he a sensitive darling? She felt bad for having fallen asleep like that. She was embarrassed but nevertheless happy that she hadn't had sex with Afanasey. She put on her green dress minus earrings and make-up. She wrote on the other side of his note: 'Thank you. It was a fairy tale: first Cinderella, then Sleeping Beauty. Talk to you soon. Sofia.'

Going downstairs, she thought she had never been a coward, it was too late to become one now. She had to thank him and say goodbye personally, not like this, leaving a scrappy note. She knocked on the door, heard some barking and some other indistinct noise, opened the door and walked in.

'Hello guys, where's your daddy?' Sofia pushed the kitchen door. It was locked. Then the door next to the kitchen opened and she saw Afanasey covering himself with a sheet and the figure of an undressed woman behind him. Sofia stepped backwards.

'I'm really sorry, Afanasey. I didn't mean to disturb you. I just wanted to thank you and say that I need to go.'

'Sofia, Sofia, I am so sorry.'

She didn't want to look at him and quickly turned away.

'Why should you be? No, honestly, I'll call you. Bye for now.'

She was at the exit in no time. On the street she started laughing uncontrollably till tears were running down her cheeks. Or was she crying in the end?

Instead of going home right away, she went into a callbox and phoned Ella. She was at home and as yet had no plans for the day so they met halfway for a cup of tea and a chat.

Sofia took her time to draw the whole panoramic picture of the events of the morning and the previous night. Ella ended up in a paroxysm of laughter.

'Bloody old satyr. Did he hurt your feelings, Sofia?'

'No, of course not. I was laughing like hell when I left. Well, to tell you the truth, it's rather strange, but I do feel awkward. It's all vanity, I suppose. You see I was such a beauty queen at the party, and he sounded as if he was in love. He made me think he had refurbished his apartment for me. What a naïve fool I am, Ella!'

'You know what, my dear, maybe he didn't lie to you. You never know with men. Take Makhmud for instance. How did such a charmer and a gentleman turn into such a bastard?'

'A wolf in sheep's clothing they call it in ancient literature.'

'Oh, damn them, men. Enough about them. I don't want to know. By the way, I have some good news for a change – I'm changing jobs. One of my old friends, just an acquaintance really, is opening his own film studio.'

'Do I know him?'

'I am sure you know him by name. It's Ivan Karetin.'

'Of course I know his films, a very gifted guy. What kind of position is it?'

'An admin director. Good salary too.'

'Fantastic, Ellochka! Do you need a personal secretary and interpreter?'

'I wish I did.'

'I'm only kidding. I'm so happy for you! So how well do you know Karetin? Is he a nice person?'

'Oh, yes. He is such a charmer ...'

'No, don't start. Please don't tell me you've fallen for him.'

'May be, just a teeny-weeny bit.'

It was a comforting chat for both of them. Now Sofia could return home cheerful and composed.

Back to Reality

November came with snowstorms and serious frost. Sofia found another part-time job. Former colleagues from the Grozny Oil Institute now working in Moscow for an American company offered her some translation work. With three jobs now, she barely had enough time to sleep, let alone for her writing.

The news from Chechnya was bad. The conflict continued to escalate. After several months of futile attempts to control the situation, the Russian government had sent in tanks. The streets of the town had been turned into a battlefield. Every day Sofia was praying for the people of Chechnya, for her own friends left in Grozny: Mila and Lena, Larissa with her daughter and mother, Nadya, Stas and Masha. There was neither telephone nor any other connection between Russia and the rebellious republic. To the great surprise of the rest of the country, the tank attack had failed. Apparently the regular army, having expected to meet a gang of thugs, had been confronted by well-trained forces. The furious commander of the Russian army threatened more radical measures. There was endless talk on television and in the Russian press about "target bombing". The general in command explained that this was a specific kind of very precise air attack. Aimed at an arsenal or barracks, for instance, the bomb would be dropped right on the object and would in no way disturb the peaceful population. In fact when the bombing actually started on December 11, 1994, the first attack destroyed the centre of the town.

That night Lisa woke them up with a cry. She had had a nightmare in which their parrot Yashka was lying on the pavement all covered with blood. Sofia warmed up some milk for her and took her into her bed, but she was shaking for another hour before going back to sleep.

Sofia's determination to celebrate New Year and Christmas as normal had only become stronger after that. It had been her own small battle and she won it. At the end of December she had everything ready: presents for the girls, Granny and Ella and even for Nelly, the dog. The girls took the New Year decorations out of the cupboard. Some of them were from the time of Sofia's childhood: an old Father Frost and a Snowgirl, some bells and candleholders. They had survived many parties. Now, reminding her of her home that had been left forever, they were here helping to restore lost happiness. That was Sofia's biggest goal: not just to live here but to live "happily ever after". 'I will make it, whatever it takes', she kept saying to herself.

Mark. Getting Ann back.

'Where are you, my darling? What has happened to you?' Mark was looking at the card Sofia had given him the day they met. He had kept it in his wallet ever since. The card was worn from his uncountable attempts to phone Chechnya. 'I wish I had your picture or something from you.'

Mark was still rather weak. His family insisted on his coming back to the UK until he was fully recovered. His brother, Peter came to Spain to help him fly back. Now he was staying at his mother's, sometimes annoyed by her care but mostly enjoying it. He was a prodigal son surrounded by everyone's concern and love.

'How are you doing today?' Peter dropped in after work, which was unusual. Mark had not seen much of him since they returned from Spain.

'Here, Mark, I've got something for you.' He handed Mark a piece of paper with a Newcastle address.

'What's this?' Mark asked, deep down knowing the answer but afraid to tempt providence.

'Ann's address. The Salvation Army helped me to trace her. Give her a call. Do you want to do it now?'

Feeling weak at the knees, Mark did not know whether to laugh or cry. He found himself doing both. His hands were shaking as he dialled the number.

'Hello,' a woman's voice answered, but he could not utter a word. Peter took the receiver. Yes, it was Ann. No, she did not remember uncle Peter. She did remember her father Mark.

'Ann, my darling, my little girl, do you know how I love you?'

'Where have you been all these years, Dad?' Ann was

crying too. 'Never mind, Dad, we'll talk about it later. I want to see you, Dad. I'm getting married next week. Will you come over to give me away?'

What a wonderful day! What a wonderful world! It was like coming back to life from oblivion for a second time. What had Sofia told him? Be ready for the moment when you meet your grown-up daughter.

The official invitation for Ann's wedding arrived by post the next day. Taking Sofia's advice, Mark spent a sleepless night in an intense imaginary conversation with Ann. He was thinking of showing her the album of her pictures he had always carried with him on his extensive journeys. He wondered if Ann had any childhood memories of their time together. If she had, she did not have time to share them with Mark when they met. He had to concentrate on looking for a little girl in a wonderful young woman hugging him and calling him "Daddy". She was there all right, his little one, in the bright dark eyes and in her smile, the cutest in the whole world. It was her, his Annie. The whole wedding weekend rocketed like fireworks. Lots of introductions and re-introductions, people everywhere. Mark and Ann hardly spent an hour alone. She never asked again why he hadn't kept in touch. Mark had prepared another serious speech for that occasion. He was going to confront Ann's mother and ask her to give her reasons why she had kept his daughter away from him. But watching Ann with her mother, he realised how close they were. Whose side would she take after all? And how could he trouble his daughter on such a day? So he decided to let bygones be bygones.

All brides are beautiful. Maybe they were, but he had only the one daughter and he knew that that moment of seeing her so blissfully pretty in her full glory as a bride would stay with him as long as he lived.

Back home, Peter did not approve of his decision when Mark told him about it.

'Why do you let your ex get away with it? You've always been a softy, Mark. At least write to Ann and explain the situation to her. Tell her about the piles of Christmas presents hidden away in her mother's wardrobe for ages till we took them to a charity shop before moving house.'

'Maybe I will, I don't know. But not now of course, she's is on her honeymoon, isn't she?'

'I thought you would be the happiest man in the world with Ann back in your life, Mark. Something's obviously still wrong with you. Is it your health? Are you in pain? Mother told me you're not sleeping well. Ask the doctor to give you some sleeping pills.'

'I'm fine, Peter, thanks for asking. I'm going back to Russia.'

'To Russia? When?'

'As soon as I have a visa.'

'May I ask is it work or something else?'

'Yes, it is something else, Peter. And her name is Sofia.'

Mark took granddad's picture with uncle Steven and Nadya out of his case and told Peter the whole story about his trip to Chechnya.

'So how are you going to find her now, when Russia has actually started a war in Chechnya?'

'A war? What are you talking about?'

'Haven't you heard the news today? Russian tanks are in Chechnya.'

'As a matter of fact, I haven't. It should be in the papers,' shouted Mark. He rushed to the nearest newsagent.

His determination to find Sofia was stronger than the

bureaucracy of the Russian Embassy in London. Mark managed to overcome the latter by buying a one-week tour to Moscow. And here he was, wasting his time, not only unable to find Sofia and her family but unable to detect the slightest trace of them anywhere. Everything he had planned to do in Moscow, like finding people who could possibly have some information about Chechnya, the Red Cross for instance or British journalists, had produced no result. He stretched himself on the bed in a very basic *en suite* room in the enormous *Rossia* hotel. The only benefit of this monstrosity was its location: it was overlooking Red Square. Clicking through the channels of his television in the hope of hearing news from Chechnya, he felt nauseous indicating that one of his now frequent headaches was not far away. It was late, ten minutes to midnight, according to the clock in his room. Mark switched off the light and tried to get some sleep.

The hotel lived according to its own timetable. This would be fine if it were not for the poor sound insulation. Lying in bed, he could hear footsteps, laughter and now even a whole conversation in broken English. His mother tongue stripped of its grammar sounded disgustingly primitive.

'Hello, you live here?' a woman's voice asked.

'Yes, I live here. You live here?' That was the voice of a man.

'You want I come in your room?' The woman's voice.

'Yes, I want you. Come in. How much?' She named the price. Unfortunately the man was his next-door neighbour. The prostitute was obviously taking her profession seriously. Noise from behind the wall suggested she was determined to give her client a full performance. Mark got out of bed, dressed and joined the night time parade along the endless corridors of his hotel. His walk, occasionally interrupted by one or another "working girl", ended up in a lift. Through a hall the size of an average football pitch, he went out into the street covered with freshly fallen snow, and in no time was in Red Square. It was the sixth of January, Russian Christmas. That was why, regardless of the late hour, there were people on the Square, even children. He noticed a woman in a big sheepskin coat and two well wrapped-up girls about the same age as Sofia's daughters. They were leaving the Square and Mark could not see their faces. What if he had known that it actually was Sofia and her girls? That night she had taken them to church and then they had insisted on having a look at Red Square. They were in a hurry to get into the underground before it closed. The girls were making jokes about their appearance. They were not used to the cold Moscow weather and their outfits consisted of items that did not go well together. Their mother, wearing an old sheepskin coat of Ella's, was the biggest laughing stock of all.

Mark's headache seemed to ease off. He continued walking round Red Square, then headed towards the *Alexandrovskiy Sad*, coming full circle through the empty alleys back to the *Rossia*. The other pain, his longing for Sofia, was always there. At the hotel reception he asked which bar was open and joined the other "sleepless in Moscow".

At the end of the week he was on his way back to London having acquired nothing but a hangover. He did not know what else he could do. If he were religious it would have been the time to pray. He wasn't. He took to drinking instead, withdrawing himself from reality, from the unfairness of a life in which he had met and lost his only true love.

173

I thought as soon as I had a more or less secure job and a place for us all to live, stability would come back, but I was mistaken. That feeling of being an "orphan in a hostile world" would creep out of the far corners of my subconscious whenever it was least expected. Along with all my compatriots, I had to learn to live with it. Without the kind of security that only a stable state could provide we were quickly regressing to a stone age, where survival was your personal responsibility. I had to fight that inner "orphan" in myself every day. But after the bombing of Grozny started I felt really proud of myself: taking my girls out of the town had been the right thing to do and I had done it in time. It helped me not to feel sorry for myself and to go on fiercely with my everyday struggle. Unfortunately my triumph was spoiled by a constant worry for the people who were still there. If it was not guilt, it was something close to it. Help them, God! In Moscow I had already met people from Grozny who had made it out of the rebellious town after the bombing started. Each had a terrifying story to tell of events there. And they went over it again and again, trapped in a circle of strong emotions, unable to make the next move. Naive "orphans" were getting together, putting what was left of their energy into writing petitions addressed to the government that had given the orders to bomb them in the first place. 'I'll be damned if I join them!' was my reaction. Besides, how could I find time for all these meetings and demonstrations? Who would provide for my family in the meantime?

When one Sunday I heard Stas on the phone it was like

having a beloved brother back.

'Stas, is that you? Where are you calling from?'

'I'm in Moscow. Larissa gave me your phone number. Can you give me your address and directions? I'll be at your place as soon as I can if you don't mind.'

'Do I mind? I can't believe I'm talking to you. Get down here straightaway. Oh, Stas, is everyone okay? Your parents? Masha?'

'All alive. I have managed to evacuate my parents with the Russian soldiers. Masha and her grandmother are still in Grozny. I need to find somewhere to move them to. Well, soon you'll have the picture in every detail. I'm on my way.'

Stas was the only one of the Grozny refugees I knew who made a kind of comedy out of his tragic experience. As if his luck in escaping from hell with his family uninjured reflected back and made him see the funny side of things. There was something of Charlie Chaplin's humour in the way he told us his story.

'I wish you had met my parents. It is actually strange that you didn't meet them because from the sixties they lived in Mendeleevskaya Street, which is very close to your Safonova Street, you know. My mother met my father during the Second World War. She was a young nurse, practically straight from school. He was a Captain, much older. He had been badly wounded in the battle of Stalingrad and was transferred to the hospital where she worked. She married him the day he was discharged from hospital. His war wounds troubled him so much that later on the doctors had to amputate both his legs. They moved to Grozny in the early fifties. I was born there. I remember the first time they took me to see our new flat on Mendeleevskaya when it was still under construction.

175

That bloody flat is to blame for my parents' late start in running away from Grozny. Every time my sister and I tried to convince them to leave, Mama, with the sweeping gesture of a landowner, would look round and say, "Go away and leave all this? You must be joking."

'The dramatic wave of her hand pointed to a display cabinet full of Czech crystal and ro the piano my sister used to torture during her seven years at music school. Both symbols of prosperity had been good for nothing but collecting dust for a number of years. Remember the prices we could get for our flats? Hardly enough to buy a garden shed elsewhere. So every time we tried to talk to them it ended up with a quarrel. My sister left a week before the bombing started. I couldn't think of leaving them alone. The situation was the same with my wife's granny. She had a tiny bungalow with an outdoor toilet and a chicken shed. Masha went to stay with her for a while, hoping to talk her into leaving. Father had his own reasons for staying. He was sure that "everything will be fine pretty soon. If the Chechens go on with the riot, the Soviet Army will sort them out".

'Mother's crystal and the piano were smashed under the ruins of the five-storey building in one of the first air raids of that same Soviet Army she and father had always considered themselves to be a part of. Thank God we had dragged father down to a cellar in one of the nearby houses. We had to stay in there for five days. The cellar was dry and spacious and full of jars of homemade preserves: pickled vegetables, compotes and jams. The people who had lived there had left everything behind. When it was quiet I went scavenging around and brought lots of useful things from the ruins, pots and pans and a kettle, some potatoes and carrots from a kitchen garden. I also gathered some wood. I had already enough to make an outdoor fire to boil the kettle, but decided to bring some to store. It was the wrong decision. I was coming round the corner of the house when I saw a man with an automatic gun crawling in my direction. He was definitely not a regular army soldier. At that very moment I realised that greed was our family's curse. Why the hell had I gone for another heap of firewood? I stood there in front of an armed bandit with my arms full, having no idea what to do or to say. He looked at me, made a noise in his throat and passed by. I dropped the bloody sticks and ran for my life. Back in the cellar, my father said, "Why is it you are never on time for a meal, Stas?" Everything was almost as usual.

'In a couple of days we saw the Russian army tanks. The soldiers were astonished to see us. They had been told there were no civilians left in the town. They promised to take my parents to Mozdok. Anywhere, out of the battle to a safe place suited me. We loaded father in his wheel chair on to a covered military truck. Mother joined him. I kissed them goodbye. I needed to make my way somehow to the bungalow where Masha and her granny had no idea if we were dead or alive. It took around three hours' walk to get there. I was relieved to see that there were no ruins in that part of the town. I found my ladies safe and sound, told them what had happened in Mendeleevskaya. Masha and I started our broken record about moving. Granny's answer to that was a pail of green paint and a brush. I was ordered to paint her outdoor toilet in this lively colour, never mind the Chechens and their political claims. Masha said, "Considering there isn't much to do anyway, and we couldn't move anywhere right now...". So there I was, a DIY war hero. The colourful comments I made whilst doing the job could have boiled the eggs in the nearby chicken shed. That was the last calm night. At dawn the bombing started again. The house was not affected but the freshly painted toilet was blasted to the ground.'

Stas's visit was short. Two months later he managed to move his wife and her stubborn granny out of town. They had been granted official refugee status and some degraded accommodation in one of the small towns of Central Russia.

We had been turned down for refugee status, but if to have it meant going through the experience of those people who stayed on in the town, I had no regrets that we had left when we did.

So we survived our first winter in Moscow.

Today is the First of March. It is supposed to be a spring month. In Grozny it would be. In Moscow it is still winter with frost and cold winds. It looks as if grey is the only colour left on God's palette. Oh, how I miss the blue sky and wet freshness of the first snowdrops! I look into the pale faces of my girls. They must miss the spring sun as much as I do, but they have never complained, my two brave companions, my little warriors. I do not need to tell them to do their homework or keep the place tidy. They are growing up quickly in Moscow. They stick together. I have never seen them play with other children or bring friends home from school as they did back in Grozny. They are probably ashamed of our shabby overcrowded flat. Never mind, at least we are not afraid that it will be destroyed by an air raid. And when we miss colours too much we just have to go to the Tretyakov Gallery or Pushkinskyi Museum and borrow some from the most talented colourists in the world. 'Okay girls? It's our way of keeping our spirits up, isn't it?' They eagerly nod their heads. God knows whether they really agree or whether they do it just to keep me happy.

But at last spring has come to the streets of Moscow, melting all the snow in April, covering parks with a lace of leafage in May, bringing back all the brightness of colours in June. Sometimes we join Afanasey at his outdoor painting sessions. It is good for the girls. I like it too. The places he chooses to paint are so beautiful.

He made some attempts to talk about that morning I saw him in bed with a woman, but there was nothing to be said. I was neither his wife nor his lover. He had imagined he was in love with me. He had definitely been mistaken. That was what I told him and I also said that I thought we were good friends. Strangely enough, his answer was: 'Sure, we are friends. As a matter of fact, that is why I think you should marry me, Sofia. You and your girls need security. Do you realise that you can't go on living here without Moscow registration? Alexandra is finishing school in a year. She won't be admitted into an Institute or a University without it. And you, my darling? How long are you going to tear yourself between three jobs? Your place is somewhere in an international firm with a good salary and a secure insurance package. And I do love you, by the way.'

Everything he said about the registration was true. If I were to consider marriage as a contract, a business agreement... Maybe I do have to think about it. But not now. I am so tired I can hardly think straight. My cousin Ella said it was a great opportunity for me.

Coming home from one of our weekends of landscape painting, we found a letter from Larissa. Granny said it had been delivered personally by an unknown lady from

179

Grozny. Granny had asked her to stay for lunch and they had spent the afternoon together.

'What they've been through is hard to believe. But let us see what Larissa has written,' said Granny.

I looked through the letter myself first so as not to give away personal details if there were any. Here it is with some insignificant changes.

Larissa's Letter

Hello Sonechka, my dear friend,

I hope I shall have time to finish this letter. I cannot miss such a rare chance for communication. We live in chaos. No running water, the electricity comes and goes whenever it suits the power station. Everything around us is either in ruins or abandoned. When the raids start we hide in a shelter left from the Second World War. It is one big mess, Sofia. The same kind of mess is in my head. Under no circumstances can I comprehend why they are doing this to us. Why are they fighting us, poor idiots who believed ourselves to be citizens of a civilised country? And another thing: why is it that our brave army is so helpless against a handful of bandits? We have heard here that there are professional terrorists from the Middle East helping the Chechens. Strangely enough, I have just written "Chechens" meaning the armed bandits who are fighting against the Russians, and in reality we are probably still alive only because of the help of a young Chechen. His name is Kazbek. We were hiding in the bomb shelter with our neighbours. There was a break in the bombing. We were not sure if it was the end of a raid or just an interval and I climbed out of the shelter to have a look. A young man, in his early twenties, definitely a Chechen, was having a cigarette outside. I was desperate for a fag. You know I never smoke in public, it is rare that a woman in Grozny does. It is like exposing yourself to an insult, isn't it? Well, I didn't care then. I asked the young man for a cig. We started talking. He said he lived two streets away. I told him where I lived. It was small talk suitable for the occasion. Did we use candles or an electric torch when there was a power cut? Where did we get our water from and how? I said we had only two pairs of hands: my teenage daughter and mine. My mother was not well enough to carry a pail of water from the street water pump twenty minutes' walk away. He said he had made a trolley using an old cycle and offered to fetch us a seven-litre canister of water. I left him our address and he kept his promise. Since then he has been helping us in every possible way. Imagine his situation and that of those Chechens like him who are not participating in the blood-shedding plot. We learnt that he was an ambulance driver working at the city hospital with his Russian girlfriend, a nurse. He insisted on her leaving Grozny. She wanted him to go with her to live with her relatives in Southern Russia, but he knew he would not be welcome there, not now when his compatriots were killing Russian soldiers in Grozny. I am giving so much space to Kazbek in my letter because it is hard to imagine how we could cope without him. He looks after all the old people and single mothers in the neighbourhood, bringing water, wood, making outdoor stoves. Amazing!

Mother and Nikusha are all right. We teach Nikusha at home whatever we can from the school subjects, mainly Russian, Maths and English. There is an old Klyuchevskyi history book that we read sometimes in turns. It gives us a sort of perspective. We do hope the conflict will be sorted out and that we are still alive when it happens.

A very big hug and kiss from Nikusha, and another one from mother.

Love, Larissa.

Later in the summer, when there was a break in the military activities in Grozny, Larissa managed to take her family out of Grozny to Mozdok, a town in Southern Russia where her mother's relatives lived. Before going back to Grozny to receive the monetary compensation promised by the Russian government for their destroyed flat, she came for a short visit to Moscow. During the three days we spent together we hardly slept because we simply could not stop talking. She told me that soon after we left, walking the empty streets of town became as dangerous as going through the jungle. Nearly every young Russian woman was either raped or suffered an attempted rape. One of our former colleagues, a German interpreter, was assaulted in her own house, another one on her way to work when she was taking a shortcut across the park. Larissa herself escaped a similar situation only because the bandit who put a knife to her throat while undoing his trousers, was interrupted by a group of people that suddenly appeared at the end of the alley. The Russian men could be beaten up. Those who drove nice cars were stopped and asked for their keys. In that case it did not matter whether it was a Russian or a Chechen. It was the car that mattered. I asked Larissa about Kazbek.

'That young man is simply a saint,' said Larissa. 'He accompanied us to the border of Chechnya to make sure we were safe. I'd like to choose a nice present for him, Sofia. Will you help me? I've heard that ordinary Chechens in the villages helped Russians who were leaving the town on foot. Gave them food and shelter. Do you remember our beautician, Irina? She had to walk all the way to the border when her house was bombed.'

So this is it. I am going to draw the line here. Do I have any answers to the questions I asked when I started writing these notes? No, I do not. Who is responsible for the bloodshed in Chechnya? And where will it end? My only conclusion is that everyone makes their own choice between right and wrong, good and evil. But it is so reassuring to know that there are always people who remain human in the most desperate circumstances. They are the hope and sanctuary for this world.

From Sofia's Diary

I am so used to writing I have decided to keep a diary now. Considering this is my first trip abroad and everything is so exciting here, I think it's worth doing. I do not know where to start. Look where I am. Oh, thank you, thank you, God. The sky is as blue as it can be. The air is full of fragrance. The sea cannot be seen from here but I feel its overwhelming presence.

An early morning phone call caught me on my way to work. It was Ella.

'Listen Sofia, do you want to go to Spain?'

'Are you joking, Ella? Can I call you later from work?'

'No, it's a serious question, dear. But I need an answer before noon. You see, we are shooting a documentary about Gaudi, you know, the one who built the *Sagrada Familia*. We are leaving for Barcelona in two weeks' time. The guy who is supposed to be my assistant and interpreter is having an urgent operation. It is a four-week trip, all expenses paid, and there is a salary of two hundred dollars. Tell the girls. I'm sure they can cope for four weeks without you. Ask for a four-week holiday from work. Come on, Sofia, move. Please dear, I need you. Otherwise the studio will send such a stupid cow with me that I'll kill myself in the first twenty four hours with her.'

'But Ella, I don't speak Spanish.'

'Neither does she. It won't stop her, so you can take the risk. Sofia, they all speak English everywhere abroad. And anyway your only encounter with the locals will be such things as calling a taxi or ordering a take-away. It doesn't mean that they, I mean the film crew, won't give you a pain in the neck in plain Russian, which often means unprintable Russian. But don't you worry, girl, I'll be there.'

I was listening to Ella's enthusiastic voice and thinking, 'In no way can I leave my girls for a whole month. And definitely under no circumstances can I pretend to know a job I have never done before. No, it's not for me.'

Ella on the other end of the line was going on about how beautiful Spain was and what unbelievable luck it was to have a holiday you were not paying for.

'Talk to the girls. Don't say anything to me now, I'm not listening. Give me a call about twelve o'clock. Bye!'

Granny and the girls, used to expecting bad news, looked out of the living room.

'Is anything wrong, Sofia? Who was that on the phone? You look excited,' asked Granny.

I told them who was calling and why.

'I think you must go, Sofia. We'll be all right. What do you think girls?'

So that was how it all started and now I am here. They are fine so far. I cannot help but start every day with a quick call to Moscow. I am still worried about them but something has happened to me here in Spain. I feel as if I have been carrying a heavy sack on my back for a very long time and suddenly it has been taken away. I feel my spine straightening and my chest taking in a deep breath of this fantastic air. Sure, I am sweating during my working day doing small chores and helping here and there: carrying parasols and chairs, holding cables, running to the nearest shops to buy water and beer, making arrangements, typing texts on a laptop, and God knows what else I might be asked to do. I've bought a Spanish conversational guide.

It helps me a lot when I feel that English is not suitable. But late evenings are all mine and they are wonderful. Tomorrow we are not shooting and I can have a whole day to myself.

I am sharing an apartment with Ella. It is on the third floor of a house called *Los Delfines* in a small village La Penida, "Pine Tree". There are some pines here too, but they are different, looking more like our Crimean pines. My bedroom has a spacious balcony, where I am sitting now, a glass of red wine in front of me. Ella is making a snack for supper. I can smell grilled peppers and garlic. She is the best companion in the world and the evening has only just started. Forget all the defeating thoughts I had in gloomy Moscow, like marrying Afanasey for instance! The night is young and full of expectation, and so is my life. Maybe somewhere not far from here on the Costa del Sol I shall meet Mark again. I can admit now that that was not the least consideration when making my decision to come to Spain. I have made some enquiries. There is a bus to Malaga. I need to make this trip even if it sounds crazy.

Mark

Mark had taken a job advertised in the *Daily Mail* a month ago. When a period of depression and drinking ended in tremendous embarrassment in front of all his family including his daughter Ann, he woke up to reality. It was time to make himself decent again. His "little girl" understood, bless her. He could not afford to lose her again. He was broke too. His mother bought him an air ticket on her credit card. In Spain his interview was successful. He was offered a job in the four star Estival Park hotel in La Penida, not far from Barcelona. His package included accommodation and food. He was comfortable in his one-bedroom flat. The Mediterranean food at the hotel restaurant was gorgeous. Soon he became friendly with some of his colleague and neighbour, a German called Michael Borman. His day was tightly scheduled. He started with jogging along the beach, followed by a coffee at the *Pastisseria* on the front. Then he kept his mind shut to everything but work till six at night. After work he met Michael for a pint. Once, watching the world news on Sky in the bar, Mark saw shots of Grozny. He could not recognise the streets. Everything was in ruins. He had to excuse himself and run out of the bar, because he knew he would be desperate to get drunk.

Later that evening, Michael tapped on his door asking him if he was all right. Mark let him in and told him his love story over a cup of good English tea. He was grateful to have a companion. He was a good man, that Michael Borman.

Now after a month in Spain he looked healthy and fit again. That morning he was having his coffee at the

Pastisseria enjoying the early hour. The smell of freshly baked bread was just starting to drift along the sleepy street. Another half hour and the doors of the tiny cafés and shops would be open, tables would be taken out on to the street and would eventually be filled, first with working folk and later on with tourists.

Mark was sitting at his usual table overlooking the front. He was the first customer of the day. The sun was still low over the sea, painting it gold. He had left his sunglasses at home and now was looking at the sea, shading his eyes with the palm of his hand. The figure of a woman outlined against the sky seemed painfully familiar. She was walking from the beach. Sofia! No, how could it be? Long hair, definitely thinner. But the way she walks... 'Am I losing my mind?' He was now on his feet running towards this woman. He had to see her more closely. That was the moment she saw him too.